w 4/
3.00
5

FOUNDATIONS OF
COMBINATORIAL TOPOLOGY

OTHER *GRAYLOCK* PUBLICATIONS

KHINCHIN: *Three Pearls of Number Theory*

NOVOZHILOV: *Foundations of the Nonlinear Theory of Elasticity*

FOUNDATIONS OF COMBINATORIAL TOPOLOGY

BY

L. S. PONTRYAGIN

GRAYLOCK PRESS

ROCHESTER, N. Y.

1952

TRANSLATED FROM THE FIRST (1947) RUSSIAN EDITION

BY

F. BAGEMIHL H. KOMM W. SEIDEL

Second Printing September 1953

Manufactured in the United States of America

CONTENTS

PREFACE

This book represents essentially a semester course in combinatorial topology which I have given several times at the Moscow National University. It contains a very rigorous but concise presentation of homology theory. The formal prerequisites are merely a few simple facts about functions of a real variable, matrices, and commutative groups. Actually, however, considerable mathematical maturity is required of the reader. An essential defect in the book is its complete omission of examples, which are so indispensable for clarifying the geometric content of combinatorial topology. In this sense a good complementary volume would be *Sketch of the Fundamental Notions of Topology* by Alexandrov and Efremovitch, in which the attention is focused on the geometric content rather than on the completeness and rigor of proofs. In spite of this shortcoming, it seems to me that the present work has certain advantages over the existing voluminous treatises, especially in view of its brevity. It can be used as a reference for obtaining preliminary information required for participation in a serious seminar on combinatorial topology. It is convenient in preparing for an examination in a course, since the proofs are carried out in the book with sufficient detail. For a more qualified reader, e.g., an aspiring mathematician, it can also serve as a source of basic information on combinatorial topology.

The present book makes use of a few facts concerning metric spaces which are now ordinarily included in a course in the theory of functions of a real variable, and which can be found in the sixth chapter of Hausdorff's *Mengenlehre* or in the third chapter of Alexandrov and Kolmogorov's *Theory of Functions of a Real Variable*. Information concerning commutative groups may be found in the fifth chapter (see §§21 and 22) of Kurosh's *Theory of Groups*.

Originally I expected to write this book jointly with Professor V. A. Efremovitch. Numerous conversations with him were very useful to me; in particular, they led to the simplification of the details of some of the proofs. In the final editing of the book, I took into account a series of remarks of V. A. Rokhlin, who kindly read my manuscript.

L. Pontryagin

INTRODUCTION

The foundations of combinatorial topology were laid at the turn of the last century by the great French mathematician Poincaré, for whom nature was the source of mathematical problems. In the greater part of his investigations, an important role is played by the geometric interpretation of analytic problems and by geometric intuition. Starting with problems in analysis, Poincaré arrived at the conclusion that it was necessary to study the geometric, and primarily the topological, properties of multi-dimensional manifolds. Initially Poincaré regarded a manifold as given by a system of equations and inequalities relative to the coordinates of a multi-dimensional Euclidean space. From this manifold he extracted, again with the aid of equations, submanifolds of smaller dimension. In this treatment there appeared already those fundamental notions which now play a leading role in combinatorial topology. If, in an n-dimensional manifold M, there exists a closed submanifold Z of smaller dimension r, $r < n$, then two cases are possible: 1) In M there exists a bounded $(r + 1)$-dimensional submanifold C whose boundary is Z; 2) In M there does not exist a submanifold C with boundary Z. In the first case, we say that Z is homologous to zero in M, and write: $Z \sim 0$ in M. In the second case, we say that Z is not homologous to zero in M.

For example, let M be the region of the plane between two concentric circumferences. If, now, we take for Z a circumference concentric with the original ones and lying in M, then it is clear that Z cannot serve as a boundary in M, and is consequently not homologous to zero in M. If, however, we take for Z a circumference which bounds a circle wholly contained in M, then $Z \sim 0$ in M. It is easy to see from this example the connection between homology and analysis. If, in the region M, an analytic function is given, then its integral along the contour Z is equal to zero when $Z \sim 0$ in M, and may not be equal to zero in the contrary case. This also indicates that it is appropriate to examine the contour Z with a prescribed sense on it, since the sign of the integral depends on the direction. An analogous connection with integration is also found in the multi-dimensional case (Stokes' formula); the sense of the contour Z is then replaced by the orientation of the manifold M.

After the first paper of Poincaré, it already became evident that the analytic treatment of manifolds, i.e., their definition with the aid of equations, leads to a series of complications, and may serve as a source of error. Poincaré then introduced a new method for the study of manifolds; he decomposed them into elementary pieces, simplexes, which adjoin one another in a regular fashion. This method has retained its significance to this day, and turns out to be fundamental in combinatorial topology. It led to the formalization of the notion of homology, whereas the homology invariants of manifolds introduced by Poincaré, Betti numbers and torsion numbers, acquired an exact logical meaning. Poincaré, however, did not succeed in establishing their topological invariance. This achievement belongs to the American mathematicians Alexander and Veblen. They also proved that the whole homology theory is applicable not only to manifolds, but also to geometric objects of a more general type, viz., polyhedra.

After Poincaré, homology theory was developed intensively. To it was added Lefschetz's theory of intersections, which was known to Poincaré only in an embryonic form. Lefschetz and Hopf proved theorems on fixed points of mappings. Alexander discovered a new duality theorem which, together with Poincaré's duality theorem, served as a basis for an extensive development of topological duality theorems, in which a large part was played by Soviet mathematicians. Soviet mathematicians also participated in the construction of cohomology theory. Finally, Alexandrov found ways of applying homology theories to set-theoretic objects, and thus arrived at a synthesis of combinatorial and set-theoretic topology.

At present, homology theory continues to develop, but the main problem now, as I see it, is its application to the solution of geometric problems into whose formulation the notion of homology itself does not enter. Some of them, such as the problem of finding sums of indices of fixed points in mapping a polyhedron into itself, have been solved completely. The solution of other problems, such as the classification of continuous mappings of one polyhedron into another, is in an embryonic state.

At the present time, homology theory, broadly understood, is a basic, well-developed, indispensable tool of combinatorial topology.

This book contains an exposition of the foundations of homology theory and of some of its applications. In Chapter I, the notions of a complex and its Betti groups are defined. In Chapter II, the topological invariance of the Betti groups is proved. Applications of homology theory are given in Chapter III: homology invariants of a continuous mapping of one polyhedron into another are constructed, and a certain sufficient condition is established for the existence of a fixed point under a continuous mapping of a polyhedron into itself.

NOTATION

In this book we assume that the reader is familiar with the important notion of set (see, e.g., Hausdorff, *Mengenlehre*). We give here certain notations connected with the concept of set and with elementary operations on sets.

A) $a \in M$ means that the element a belongs to the set M. If the set M is finite or enumerable, then we shall sometimes specify the set by means of a simple enumeration of its elements; in symbols:

$$M = \{a_1, \cdots, a_n, \cdots\}.$$

This means that the set M consists of the elements $a_1, \cdots, a_n, \cdots$.

B) $M = N$ means that the sets M and N are identical.

C) $M \subset N$ or $N \supset M$ means that every element of the set M belongs to the set N, i.e., that the set M is a part, or subset, of the set N. The possibility that the two sets are identical is not excluded.

D) $M \cap N$ denotes the *intersection* of the sets M and N, i.e., the set of all elements which belong to both M and N.

E) $M \cup N$ denotes the *union* of the sets M and N, i.e., the set of all elements belonging to at least one of the sets M, N.

F) $M \setminus N$ denotes the *difference* between the sets M and N, i.e., the set of all elements of M which do not belong to N. Thus the operation of subtraction is possible independently of whether N is a subset of M or not. If $M \subset N$, then the result of the above subtraction is the *empty* set, i.e., the set containing no elements.

G) Let M and N be two sets. Suppose that to every element x in the set M there corresponds a definite element $y = f(x)$ in the set N. We call this correspondence a *mapping* f of the set M *into* the set N. The element y is called the *image* of the element x under the mapping f, and the element x is called the *inverse image* or one of the inverse images of the element y. We say that f is a mapping of the set M *onto* the set N if every element b of N has at least one inverse image a under the mapping f, i.e., $b = f(a)$. If A is a subset of the set M, i.e., $A \subset M$, $f(A)$ denotes the set of all those elements in N which are images of elements in A; $f(A)$ is called the *image of the set* A. If $B \subset N$, then $f^{-1}(B)$ denotes the set of all those elements in M which go over into elements of B under the mapping f; $f^{-1}(B)$ is called the *complete inverse image of the set* B under the mapping f. The mapping f of the set M onto the set N is called *one-to-one* if every element of the set N has only one inverse image under the mapping f. If f is a one-to-one mapping, the equation $y = f(x)$ has a unique solution x, i.e., knowing the element y, x can be determined uniquely, and we have $x = f^{-1}(y)$. The mapping f^{-1} is called the *inverse* of the mapping f.

H) This book presupposes a knowledge of metric spaces (see Hausdorff, *Mengenlehre*). The distance between the points x and y of a metric space will be denoted by $\rho(x, y)$. The distance between the subsets A and B of a metric space will be denoted by $\rho(A, B)$. It is possible to understand the book, with the exception of §3, if one interprets metric space as an arbitrary subset of a Euclidean space of an arbitrary number of dimensions, and regards as the distance between two points of this subset their ordinary Euclidean distance.

Chapter I

COMPLEXES AND THEIR BETTI GROUPS

Combinatorial topology studies geometric forms by decomposing them into the simplest geometric figures, simplexes, which adjoin one another in a regular fashion. A geometric figure which can be decomposed into simplexes in the appropriate way is called a polyhedron, and the scheme of decomposition itself is called a complex. To begin with, the study of a polyhedron is confined to a search for its topological invariants. The investigation starts with some decomposition of the polyhedron into simplexes, i.e., with a complex which determines the polyhedron. The problem of constructing a complete system of topological invariants of a polyhedron has by no means been solved. As yet only several invariants have been constructed and studied. Among these, the Betti groups, also known as the homology groups, are the most significant. The Betti groups are commutative and admit of finite systems of generators. They can, therefore, be determined by their numerical invariants. These same numerical invariants were originally introduced by Poincaré as topological invariants of polyhedra. Later, under the influence of the ideas of modern algebra, it was found more expedient to start with an examination of the groups themselves, rather than with their numerical invariants. Application of the group-theoretic approach to polyhedra gave only some advantages in exposition. In the transition to geometric forms more general than polyhedra, however, it also made possible the investigation of group invariants not reducible to numbers.

This chapter is concerned basically with the definition of a complex and the construction of its Betti groups. The proof of the invariance of the Betti groups will be given in the following chapter.

The complex, arising initially as a scheme of decomposition of a polyhedron, now plays a more significant role in topology; in particular, it leads to important applications in set-theoretic topology, one of which is given in §3.

§1. Euclidean space

We shall state here several properties of Euclidean space which are needed in the sequel.

Linear Space

DEFINITION 1. A set R^n of elements, referred to as *points* or *vectors,* is called a *linear* or *vector space* of dimension n, if it satisfies the following conditions:

1. The set R^n forms a commutative group under addition.

2. The set R^n is a module over the field of real numbers, i.e., multiplication of the elements of R^n by real numbers can be defined to satisfy the conditions: if λ and μ are arbitrary real numbers, and x and y are arbitrary vectors of R^n, then

$$\lambda(x + y) = \lambda x + \lambda y, \qquad (\lambda + \mu)x = \lambda x + \mu x,$$
$$\lambda(\mu x) = (\lambda\mu)x, \qquad 1 \cdot x = x, \qquad 0 \cdot x = 0.$$

3. The maximum number of linearly independent elements of R^n is equal to n.

As usual, a system $x_1, \cdots, x_k$ of elements of R^n is called *linearly independent* if the relation

$$\lambda^1 x_1 + \cdots + \lambda^k x_k = 0, \tag{1}$$

where $\lambda^1, \cdots, \lambda^k$ are real numbers, implies that

$$\lambda^1 = \cdots = \lambda^k = 0. \tag{2}$$

A maximal system $e_1, \cdots, e_n$ of linearly independent elements of the n-dimensional linear space R^n is called a *basis* of R^n. It is possible to introduce coordinates by means of a chosen basis in R^n: if x is an element of R^n, there exists a dependence relation $\lambda x + \lambda^1 e_1 + \cdots + \lambda^n e_n = 0$, because the system $e_1, \cdots, e_n$ is maximal. Here $\lambda \neq 0$, since a basis is linearly independent. Solving this relation for x, we get

$$x = x^1 e_1 + \cdots + x^n e_n, \tag{3}$$

where $x^1, \cdots, x^n$ are real numbers, referred to as the coordinates of the vector x with respect to the basis $e_1, \cdots, e_n$. We shall write x in terms of its coordinates as

$$x = (x^1, \cdots, x^n). \tag{4}$$

A) A system of points $x_0, x_1, \cdots, x_k$ of an n-dimensional linear space R^n is called *independent* if the system of vectors

$$(x_1 - x_0), \cdots, (x_k - x_0) \tag{5}$$

is linearly independent. It is clear that independence is possible only for $k \leqq n$. It turns out that the system (5) is linearly independent if, and only if, the relations

$$\lambda^0 x_0 + \lambda^1 x_1 + \cdots + \lambda^k x_k = 0, \tag{6}$$

$$\lambda^0 + \lambda^1 + \cdots + \lambda^k = 0 \tag{7}$$

imply that

$$\lambda^0 = \lambda^1 = \cdots = \lambda^k = 0, \tag{8}$$

where $\lambda^0, \lambda^1, \cdots, \lambda^k$ are real numbers.

Hence the independence of a system of points $x_0, x_1, \cdots, x_k$ does not depend on the order in which the points are enumerated. Moreover, it is clear that the independence of a system of points implies the independence of every one of its subsystems.

We shall show that, given the linear independence of the system of vectors (5), relation (8) follows from (6) and (7). By (7), we can rewrite (6) in the form

$$-(\lambda^1 + \cdots + \lambda^k)x_0 + \lambda^1 x_1 + \cdots + \lambda^k x_k = 0,$$

or

$$\lambda^1(x_1 - x_0) + \cdots + \lambda^k(x_k - x_0) = 0.$$

Since the system (5) is linearly independent, the last relation implies that $\lambda^1 = \cdots = \lambda^k = 0$, and hence, in view of (7), it also follows that $\lambda^0 = 0$. Let us now prove that if (8) follows from (6) and (7), then the system (5) is linearly independent. Let us assume that

$$\lambda^1(x_1 - x_0) + \cdots + \lambda^k(x_k - x_0) = 0. \tag{9}$$

Setting $\lambda^0 = -(\lambda^1 + \cdots + \lambda^k)$, we can rewrite (9) in the form

$$\lambda^0 x_0 + \lambda^1 x_1 + \cdots + \lambda^k x_k = 0,$$

where the numbers $\lambda^0, \lambda^1, \cdots, \lambda^k$ satisfy condition (7). Hence, by assumption, $\lambda^0 = \lambda^1 = \cdots = \lambda^k = 0$, i.e., it follows from (9) that

$$\lambda^1 = \cdots = \lambda^k = 0,$$

which means that the system (5) is linearly independent.

Geometrically, the independence of the points $x_0, x_1, \cdots, x_k$ means that the hyperplane of least dimension which spans them is of dimension k. If the points $x_0, x_1, \cdots, x_k$ are dependent, the hyperplane of least dimension which spans them has dimension less than k. We shall now give another criterion for the independence of points.

B) Let $x_0, x_1, \cdots, x_k$, $k \leqq n$, be a system of points of an n-dimensional linear space R^n, and $e_1, \cdots, e_n$ a basis of this space. The coordinates of our points are determined by the relation

$$x_i = x^1{}_i e_1 + \cdots + x^n{}_i e_n, \qquad i = 0, 1, \cdots, k. \tag{10}$$

Now introduce formally the numbers $x^0{}_i$ by setting

$$x^0{}_i = 1, \qquad i = 0, 1, \cdots, k. \tag{11}$$

Denote the matrix $\| x^j_i \|$, $i = 0, 1, \cdots, k$; $j = 0, 1, \cdots, n$, by

$$N(x_0, x_1, \cdots, x_k) = N(X).$$

It has $k + 1$ rows and $n + 1$ columns, $k + 1 \leqq n + 1$. We shall prove that the points $x_0, x_1, \cdots, x_k$ are independent if, and only if, the matrix $N(X)$ is of rank $k + 1$.

If the rank of the matrix $N(X)$ is less than $k + 1$, there is a linear dependence among its rows, i.e., there are $k + 1$ numbers $\lambda^0, \lambda^1, \cdots, \lambda^k$, not all equal to zero, for which

$$\lambda^0 x^j_0 + \lambda^1 x^j_1 + \cdots + \lambda^k x^j_k = 0, \quad j = 0, 1, \cdots, n. \tag{12}$$

Multiplying relation (10) by λ^i and summing over i, we get, by (12),

$$\lambda^0 x_0 + \lambda^1 x_1 + \cdots + \lambda^k x_k = \textstyle\sum_{j=1}^n (\lambda^0 x^j_0 + \lambda^1 x^j_1 + \cdots + \lambda^k x^j_k) e_j = 0.$$

For $j = 0$, relation (12), in virtue of (11), gives $\lambda^0 + \lambda^1 + \cdots + \lambda^k = 0$. Hence the points $x_0, x_1, \cdots, x_k$ are dependent (see (6), (7) of A)).

Let us assume that the points $x_0, x_1, \cdots, x_k$ are dependent. Then there are $k + 1$ numbers $\lambda^0, \lambda^1, \cdots, \lambda^k$ which do not all vanish and which satisfy (6) and (7). Substituting into (6) the expression for x_i given in formula (10) and rewriting (7) in the form $\lambda^0 x^0_0 + \lambda^1 x^0_1 + \cdots + \lambda^k x^0_k = 0$ (see (11)), we obtain (12). However, this means that the rank of the matrix $N(X)$ is less than $k + 1$.

It is very easy to find an independent system of points $u_0, u_1, \cdots, u_k$, $k \leqq n$, in an n-dimensional space R^n. For, if $e_1, \cdots, e_n$ is a basis of R^n, it suffices to put

$$u_0 = 0, \quad u_1 = e_1, \cdots, \quad u_k = e_k. \tag{13}$$

Here $u_0 = 0$ is the zero of the group R^n, or equivalently, the origin of coordinates of the linear space R^n. The vectors

$$(u_1 - u_0) = e_1, \cdots, (u_k - u_0) = e_k$$

are obviously linearly independent; hence, by A), the points $u_0, u_1, \cdots, u_k$ are independent. We shall answer the question concerning the existence of independent points more fully in C). In this connection we shall use the notion of proximity of points in R^n in the sense of the proximity of their coordinates.

C) If $x_0, x_1, \cdots, x_k$, $k \leqq n$, is a system of points of an n-dimensional linear space R^n, then an arbitrary neighborhood of each point x_i contains a point y_i such that the system $y_0, y_1, \cdots, y_k$ is independent.

We shall apply B) to prove C). Let $u_0, u_1, \cdots, u_k$ be a system of points known to be independent (see (13)), and let t, $0 \leqq t \leqq 1$, be a real parameter.

Consider the points determined by

$$z_i(t) = tu_i + (1 - t)x_i, \qquad i = 0, 1, \cdots, k. \tag{14}$$

It is easily verified that the matrix $N(Z(t))$ associated with the system of points (14) is related to the matrices $N(X)$ and $N(U)$ of the initial systems of points by the equation

$$N(Z(t)) = tN(U) + (1 - t)N(X). \tag{15}$$

Since the points $u_0, u_1, \cdots, u_k$ are independent, it follows from B) that the rank of the matrix $N(U)$ is equal to $k + 1$. Hence the matrix $N(U)$ contains a non-vanishing determinant of $k + 1$ columns. Let $D(t)$ be the corresponding determinant of $N(Z(t))$, the notation emphasizing its dependence on the parameter t. Since $N(Z(1)) = N(U)$ (see (15)), $D(1) \neq 0$, and therefore $D(t)$ does not vanish identically in t. Since $D(t)$ is a polynomial in t, there is an arbitrarily small positive number s for which $D(s) \neq 0$. This means that the matrix $N(Z(s))$ is of rank $k + 1$, and hence $y_0 = z_0(s), y_1 = z_1(s), \cdots, y_k = z_k(s)$ form an independent system of points. The point y_i is arbitrarily close to x_i (see (14)), in view of the arbitrary smallness of s.

DEFINITION 2. A system of points $x_0, x_1, \cdots, x_m$ of an n-dimensional linear space R^n is said to be in *general position*, if each of its subsystems of $k + 1$ points $\xi_0, \xi_1, \cdots, \xi_k$ ($k \leqq n$) is independent (see A)).

It is clear that, if $m \leqq n$, generality of position is equivalent to independence. If $m \geqq n$, in order that a system be in general position, it is sufficient that every one of its subsystems of exactly $n + 1$ points ($k = n$) be independent.

We shall show that, for every positive integer m, there is a system of $m + 1$ points in general position. However, the proof of this fact is more conveniently carried out by the use of a metric, and will therefore be postponed until we have defined a Euclidean space.

Linear Euclidean Space

DEFINITION 3. A linear space R^n is called *Euclidean* if there exists in R^n an operation known as *scalar multiplication*, i.e., an operation which associates with every two vectors x and y of R^n a real number xy, their scalar product, and which is *linear*, *symmetric*, and *nonnegative:*

$$(\lambda x + \mu y)z = \lambda xz + \mu yz, \qquad xy = yx, \qquad xx \geqq 0,$$

where, in the last relation, equality occurs only if $x = 0$.

Two vectors x and y are said to be *orthogonal* if their scalar product is zero, $xy = 0$.

We remark that it is possible to introduce a scalar product in every linear space R^n. In fact, if $e_1, \cdots, e_n$ is a basis of R^n, define the scalar product for the basis vectors by putting $e_i e_j = \delta_{ij}(\delta_{ii} = 1, \delta_{ij} = 0$ for $i \neq j)$. If $x = x^1 e_1 + \cdots + x^n e_n$ and $y = y^1 e_1 + \cdots + y^n e_n$ are any two vectors of R^n, then to satisfy the conditions postulated for the scalar product, we must have

$$xy = x^1 y^1 + \cdots + x^n y^n. \tag{16}$$

It is easily verified that the scalar product defined by the last relation satisfies all the requirements of Def. 3.

D) It is always possible to introduce an *orthonormal basis* in the Euclidean space R^n, i.e., a basis $e_1, \cdots, e_n$ such that $e_i e_j = \delta_{ij}$. It is clear that if the basis is orthonormal, the scalar product in coordinate form is given by formula (16).

We shall start with an arbitrary basis $x_1, \cdots, x_n$ of the space R^n and construct an orthonormal basis from it. Since $x_1, \cdots, x_n$ is a basis, $x_1 \neq 0$, and hence $x_1 x_1 \neq 0$. We can therefore put $e_1 = (x_1 x_1)^{-\frac{1}{2}} x_1$, so that $e_1 e_1 = 1$. Now assume that the system $e_1, \cdots, e_k$, $e_i e_j = \delta_{ij}$, $k < n$, has already been constructed, with all its elements expressed linearly in terms of the vectors $x_1, \cdots, x_k$. In view of this, the vector

$$y = x_{k+1} - (\lambda^1 e_1 + \cdots + \lambda^k e_k)$$

differs from zero. Choose the numbers $\lambda^1, \cdots, \lambda^k$ so that $y e_i = 0$, $i = 1, \cdots, k$; for this it suffices to set $\lambda^i = x_{k+1} e_i$. Since $y \neq 0$, we may put $e_{k+1} = (yy)^{-\frac{1}{2}} y$, with the result that $e_i e_j = \delta_{ij}$, $i, j = 1, \cdots, k+1$. In this manner, the system $e_1, \cdots, e_n$ is constructed. Since it is orthonormal, it is obviously linearly independent. Indeed, scalar multiplication of the relation $\lambda^1 e_1 + \cdots + \lambda^n e_n = 0$ by e_i yields $\lambda^i = 0$.

E) A *metric* which satisfies all three axioms of a metric space can be introduced in the Euclidean space R^n by setting

$$\rho(x, y) = +[(x - y)(x - y)]^{\frac{1}{2}}.$$

By the axioms defining the scalar product (see Def. 3), $\rho(x, y) = 0$ if, and only if, $x = y$; furthermore, $\rho(x, y) = \rho(y, x)$. To prove the *triangle axiom*, i.e.,

$$[(x - y)(x - y)]^{\frac{1}{2}} + [(y - z)(y - z)]^{\frac{1}{2}} \geqq [(x - z)(x - z)]^{\frac{1}{2}},$$

set $x - y = u$, $y - z = v$ and rewrite the axiom in the form

$$[uu]^{\frac{1}{2}} + [vv]^{\frac{1}{2}} \geqq [(u + v)(u + v)]^{\frac{1}{2}}.$$

Since both sides of this relation are nonnegative, it is equivalent to the relation

$$uu + 2[(uu)(vv)]^{\frac{1}{2}} + vv \geqq uu + 2uv + vv,$$

which in turn is equivalent to

$$(uu)(vv) \geqq (uv)^2. \tag{17}$$

Relation (17), the so-called *Schwarz inequality*, will now be proved.

The quadratic form

$$(uu)\lambda^2 + 2(uv)\lambda + (vv) = (\lambda u + v)(\lambda u + v)$$

is nonnegative, since it is the scalar square of the vector $\lambda u + v$. Hence its discriminant $(uu)(vv) - (uv)^2$ is nonnegative, which means that relation (17) is always valid.

We return now to the question of the general position of points (see Def. 2).

THEOREM 1. *If* $\{x_0, x_1, \cdots, x_m\} = S$ *is a system of points in general position in the Euclidean space* R^n, *then there exists a positive* ε *such that* $\rho(x_i, y_i) < \varepsilon$, $i = 0, 1, \cdots, m$, *implies that the system of points* $y_0, y_1, \cdots, y_m$ *is also in general position.*

Proof. Let $\xi_i = x_{p_i}$, $i = 0, 1, \cdots, k$; $k \leqq n$, be an arbitrary subsystem S' of the system S. The system S' is independent by definition, and hence the matrix $N(\xi_0, \xi_1, \cdots, \xi_k)$ (see B)) is of rank $k + 1$. Therefore one of the determinants, say D, composed of $k + 1$ columns of this matrix, is different from zero. Since D is a continuous function of the coordinates of the points of the system S', there is a positive ε' such that for every system of points $\eta_i = y_{p_i}$, $i = 0, 1, \cdots, k$, with $\rho(\xi_i, \eta_i) < \varepsilon'$, the determinant D formed for the points $\eta_0, \eta_1, \cdots, \eta_k$ is also different from zero. Hence the matrix $N(\eta_0, \eta_1, \cdots, \eta_k)$ is of rank $k + 1$, which means that the system $\eta_0, \eta_1, \cdots, \eta_k$ is independent. Thus a suitable ε' can be assigned to every subsystem S' of the system S, and the required ε of the theorem can be obtained by setting ε equal to the smallest of the numbers ε'.

THEOREM 2. *If* $\{x_0, x_1, \cdots, x_m\} = S$ *is any system of points of the Euclidean space* R^n, *and* ε *is a positive number, then there exists a system of points* $y_0, y_1, \cdots, y_m$ *in general position such that* $\rho(x_i, y_i) < \varepsilon$, $i = 0, 1, \cdots, m$. *In other words, any finite system of points of* R^n *can be brought into general position by an arbitrarily small displacement.*

Proof. Let us number all subsystems $\xi_0, \xi_1, \cdots, \xi_k$, $k \leqq n$, of the system S, denoting them by $S_1, \cdots, S_r$. The system S_1 contains at most $n + 1$ points, and it can therefore be transformed into an independent system by an arbitrarily small displacement (see C)). Now suppose that, by means of arbitrarily small displacements of the whole system S, we have already obtained a position for which all the subsystems $S_1, \cdots, S_s$, $s < r$, are independent. By C), the system S_{s+1} can also be transformed into an independent one by an arbitrarily small displacement, and this displacement can therefore be chosen so small that the independence of the systems $S_1, \cdots, S_s$ achieved previously will not be disturbed (see Theorem 1). This completes the induction, and the theorem is proved.

Convex Bodies

We shall present here some facts concerning convex bodies needed in the sequel.

F) Let a and b be two distinct points of the Euclidean space R^n. The set of all points $x \in R^n$ of the form $x = \lambda a + \mu b$, where λ and μ are real numbers satisfying the conditions

$$\lambda + \mu = 1, \qquad \lambda \geqq 0, \qquad \mu \geqq 0,$$

will be called the *segment* $(a, b) = (b, a)$ with endpoints a and b. The two parameters λ and μ can be replaced by a single parameter $s = \mu$, $0 \leqq s \leqq 1$, in terms of which a point of the segment can be written in the form

$$(18) \qquad x = (1 - s)a + sb = a + s(b - a) = a + su, \qquad u = b - a.$$

If the segments (a, b) and (a, c) have a common point different from a, then one of the segments is contained in the other; in particular, the segments may coincide, in which case $b = c$.

To prove this assertion, let us write the points of both segments in the form (18)

$$x = a + su, \qquad 0 \leqq s \leqq 1; \qquad y = a + tv, \qquad 0 \leqq t \leqq 1.$$

If $x_0 = y_0 \neq a$ is a point common to the two segments, then

$$x_0 = a + s_0 u = y_0 = a + t_0 v, \qquad s_0 \neq 0, \qquad t_0 \neq 0,$$

and

$$s_0 u = t_0 v.$$

If $s_0 = t_0$, then $u = v$, $b = c$, and the segments coincide. If $s_0 \neq t_0$, then, assuming for definiteness that $s_0 < t_0$, we have $v = (s_0/t_0)u$, and any point y of the segment (a, c) is of the form $y = a + t(s_0/t_0)u$. Since $(s_0/t_0) < 1$, $y \in (a, b)$ for $0 \leqq t \leqq 1$, and the second segment is a proper subset of the first.

G) A set M of points of the Euclidean space R^n is called *convex* if $a \in M$, $b \in M$ implies $(a, b) \subset M$. The point a is called an *interior* point of the set M if there exists a positive ε such that $\rho(a, x) < \varepsilon$ implies $x \in M$. A convex set W which is compact and contains interior points will be referred to as a *convex body*. The set U of all interior points of a convex body W clearly forms an open set in R^n, and hence $V = W \backslash U$ is compact. The set V is called the *frontier* of the convex body W. If $a \in U$, and b and c are two distinct points of V, then the segments (a, b) and (a, c) have only one common point a. Furthermore, if $a \in U$ and c is any point of W, then there is a point $b \in V$ such that the segment (a, b) contains c.

To prove the above, we shall show first that if $a \in U$, $b \in W$, then every point c of the segment (a, b) distinct from b is contained in U. Let $c = \lambda a + \mu b$, $\lambda \neq 0$. Since $a \in U$, there is a positive ε such that $(a + x) \in W$ for $xx < \varepsilon^2$. Hence the segment $(a + x, b)$ is wholly contained in W, and therefore also the point

$$\lambda(a + x) + \mu b = \lambda a + \mu b + \lambda x = c + \lambda x \in W.$$

If now y is an arbitrary vector of R^n, with $yy < \lambda^2\varepsilon^2$, then the point $c + y$ is of the form $c + \lambda x$, where $xx < \varepsilon^2$. But under this condition, $c + \lambda x$ belongs to W, and hence $c \in U$.

Now let $a \in U$, and let b and c be two distinct points of V. If the segments (a, b) and (a, c) have a common point different from a, then, by F), either they coincide and $b = c$, which is impossible, or one of them forms a proper subset of the other. If, say, $(a, c) \subset (a, b)$, then $c \in (a, b)$, with $c \neq b$. Hence $c \in U$ and $c \notin V$, which is a contradiction.

Now let $a \in U$, and let c be any point of W distinct from a. We shall determine the segment (a, b), $b \in V$, which contains c. Set $c - a = v$ and consider the set of all points y of R^n of the form $y = a + tv$, $t \geqq 0$. If t is sufficiently small, y is evidently in U, since a is an interior point of W. On the other hand, if t is sufficiently large, y cannot be in W since W is compact. Hence the compactness of W implies that there is a largest positive value $t = t_0$ for which $y \in W$. It is clear that $a + t_0v = b$ is a frontier point of W; for otherwise, t_0 would not be maximal.

Since $c = a + v \in W$, it follows that $t_0 \geqq 1$. Setting $t_0v = u$, the set of all points of the segment (a, b) can be written in the form $x = a + su$, $0 \leqq s \leqq 1$. The point c is of the form $a + (1/t_0)u$, $0 < (1/t_0) \leqq 1$, and therefore belongs to the segment (a, b).

Since a convex body contains an interior point a, it also contains other interior points. All of these must lie on segments of the form (a, b), $b \in V$, and therefore V is non-vacuous. If $c = a$, the point c lies on an arbitrary segment (a, b), $b \in V$. This proves G).

§2. Simplex. Complex. Polyhedron

Combinatorial topology studies geometric figures, decomposing them in some regular fashion into the simplest figures, simplexes. Those geometrical figures which can be decomposed in a suitable manner into simplexes are called polyhedra, and the scheme of decomposition into simplexes is known as a complex. This section is devoted to the definition of these basic concepts.

Simplex

DEFINITION 4. Let $a_0, a_1, \cdots, a_r$ be a system of independent points of the n-dimensional Euclidean space R^n, $r \leqq n$ (see §1, A)). The set A^r of the points x of the space R^n of the form

$$x = \lambda^0 a_0 + \lambda^1 a_1 + \cdots + \lambda^r a_r, \tag{1}$$

where $\lambda^0, \lambda^1, \cdots, \lambda^r$ are real numbers which satisfy the conditions

$$\lambda^0 + \lambda^1 + \cdots + \lambda^r = 1, \tag{2}$$

$$\lambda^i \geqq 0, \qquad i = 0, 1, \cdots, r, \tag{3}$$

is called an r-dimensional *simplex*, or briefly, an r-simplex. We write $A^r = (a_0, a_1, \cdots, a_r)$. The points $a_0, a_1, \cdots, a_r$, called *vertices*, are obviously contained in the simplex A^r.

It will be shown below that if two simplexes A^r and B^s coincide, $A^r = B^s$, then their vertices also coincide, except possibly for a permutation; and, in particular, $r = s$. Furthermore, as a consequence of (1) and (2), the point x uniquely determines the numbers $\lambda^0, \lambda^1, \cdots, \lambda^r$. This enables us to regard the numbers $\lambda^0, \lambda^1, \cdots, \lambda^r$, which satisfy (2) and (3), as the coordinates (*barycentric coordinates*) of the point $x \in A^r$.

We show first that (1) and (2) uniquely define the numbers $\lambda^0, \lambda^1, \cdots, \lambda^r$. If

$$x = \mu^0 a_0 + \mu^1 a_1 + \cdots + \mu^r a_r, \tag{4}$$

where

$$\mu^0 + \mu^1 + \cdots + \mu^r = 1, \tag{5}$$

then subtraction of (1) from (4) yields

$$(\mu^0 - \lambda^0)a_0 + (\mu^1 - \lambda^1)a_1 + \cdots + (\mu^r - \lambda^r)a_r = 0.$$

Relations (2) and (5) imply that

$$(\mu^0 - \lambda^0) + (\mu^1 - \lambda^1) + \cdots + (\mu^r - \lambda^r) = 0,$$

and since the points $a_0, a_1, \cdots, a_r$ are independent, $\mu^i - \lambda^i = 0$, i.e.,

$$\mu^i = \lambda^i, \qquad i = 0, 1, \cdots, r.$$

Let us now show that the vertices $a_0, a_1, \cdots, a_r$ are uniquely determined by the set A^r. If u_0 and u_1 are two distinct points of R^n, then $x = \frac{1}{2}(u_0 + u_1)$ is the midpoint of the segment (u_0, u_1). It turns out that every point x of the simplex A^r, which is not a vertex, is the midpoint of some segment whose endpoints belong to A^r. The vertices of A^r, however, cannot be midpoints of segments with endpoints in A^r.

If $x = \lambda^0 a_0 + \lambda^1 a_1 + \cdots + \lambda^r a_r$ is any point of A^r and not a vertex of A^r, then at least two of its barycentric coordinates, say $\lambda^i, \lambda^j, i \neq j$, do not vanish, so that $\lambda^i > 0, \lambda^j > 0$. Choose an ε such that $0 < \varepsilon < \lambda^i, 0 < \varepsilon < \lambda^j$, and set $u_0 = x + \varepsilon\,(a_i - a_j)$, $u_1 = x - \varepsilon\,(a_i - a_j)$. The points u_0 and u_1 evidently belong to A^r, and

$$x = \tfrac{1}{2}(u_0 + u_1).$$

If $a_k = \frac{1}{2}(u_0 + u_1)$, where u_0 and u_1 are two distinct points of A^r, and

$$u_p = \lambda^0_{\ p}\, a_0 + \cdots + \lambda^r_{\ p}\, a_r\,, \qquad p = 0, 1,$$

then, since the points u_0 and u_1 are distinct, there are two integers i, j, $i \neq j$, for which $\lambda^i_{\ 0} > 0$ and $\lambda^j_{\ 1} > 0$. By assumption,

$$a_k = \tfrac{1}{2}(\lambda^0_{\ 0} + \lambda^0_{\ 1})\, a_0 + \cdots + \tfrac{1}{2}(\lambda^r_{\ 0} + \lambda^r_{\ 1})\, a_r\,,$$

where $\frac{1}{2}(\lambda^i_{\ 0} + \lambda^i_{\ 1}) > 0$, $\frac{1}{2}(\lambda^j_{\ 0} + \lambda^j_{\ 1}) > 0$. This contradicts the previous proof of the uniqueness of the coordinates of the points of a simplex, since

$$a_k = 0 \cdot a_0 + \cdots + 1 \cdot a_k + \cdots + 0 \cdot a_r\,.$$

By Def. 4, a 0-simplex (a_0) consists of one point a_0 . A 1-simplex (a_0, a_1) represents the rectilinear segment connecting the points a_0 and a_1 . A 2-simplex $(a_0\,, a_1\,, a_2)$ consists of the triangle with vertices $a_0\,, a_1\,, a_2$. Finally, a 3-simplex $(a_0\,, a_1\,, a_2\,, a_3)$ is a tetrahedron with vertices $a_0\,, a_1\,, a_2\,, a_3$.

A) If $A^r \subset R^n$ is an r-simplex, then a point $x \in A^r$, all of whose barycentric coordinates are positive, is called an *interior* point of the simplex A^r. A point of A^r which is not an interior point of the simplex A^r is called a *frontier* point of A^r. The set G^r of all interior points of the simplex is called an r-dimensional *open* simplex, or simply, an open r-simplex; and the set F^{r-1} of all frontier points of the simplex A^r is referred to as its *frontier*. It is easily verified that the closure $\bar{G}^r$ of an open simplex G^r coincides with the initial simplex A^r; and since A^r is a bounded closed set in R^n, it is compact. The set F^{r-1} is also obviously closed in A^r, and therefore $G^r = A^r \backslash F^{r-1}$ is an open set in A^r. If G^r and H^s are two open simplexes which coincide, $G^r = H^s$, then $\bar{G}^r = \bar{H}^s$; and since $\bar{G}^r$ and $\bar{H}^s$ are the usual (closed) simplexes, their vertices coincide and $r = s$. Hence an open simplex determines its vertices uniquely.

B) Let R^{r+1} be the $(r + 1)$-dimensional Euclidean space, $e_0\,, e_1\,, \cdots, e_r$ an orthonormal system of points (vectors) in R^{r+1} (see §1), and $E^r = (e_0\,, e_1\,, \cdots\,, e_r) \subset R^{r+1}$ the r-simplex with these points as vertices. Every point $z \in E^r$ is of the form $z = \lambda^0 e_0 + \lambda^1 e_1 + \cdots + \lambda^r e_r$ with the λ^i's satisfying (2) and (3). Since $e_0\,, e_1\,, \cdots\,, e_r$ is an orthonormal system, the Euclidean coordinates of the point z relative to this system are the same as its barycentric coordinates in E^r, and we may write

$$z = (\lambda^0, \lambda^1, \cdots, \lambda^r) = \lambda.$$

Hence the distance between two points λ and μ of E^r is given by

$$\rho(\lambda, \mu) = [(\lambda^0 - \mu^0)^2 + (\lambda^1 - \mu^1)^2 + \cdots + (\lambda^r - \mu^r)^2]^{\frac{1}{2}}.$$

The resulting metric of this r-simplex, called its *natural* metric, is a function of the intrinsic (barycentric) coordinates of the simplex. Relation (1), which associates the point $\lambda \in E^r$ with the point $x \in A^r$, is obviously continuous and one-to-one; and since E^r is compact, this correspondence is bicontinuous. Hence every two r-simplexes are homeomorphic, and this homeomorphism may be realized by the mapping which associates points having identical barycentric coordinates.

C) Let $A^r = (a_0, a_1, \cdots, a_r)$ be an r-simplex in R^n, and $\alpha_k = a_{i_k}$, $k = 0, 1, \cdots, s$; $0 \leqq s \leqq r$, a subset of the vertices of A^r. Since the vertices $a_0, a_1, \cdots, a_r$ are independent, the vertices $\alpha_0, \alpha_1, \cdots, \alpha_s$ are also independent, and hence $C^s = (\alpha_0, \alpha_1, \cdots, \alpha_s)$ is a simplex in R^n. The simplex C^s will be referred to as an *s-dimensional face*, or simply *s-face*, of the simplex A^r. Denoting those of the numbers $0, 1, \cdots, r$ which are different from $i_0, i_1, \cdots, i_s$ by $j_1, \cdots, j_{r-s}$, an arbitrary point $x \in C^s$ is obtained by putting

$$(6) \qquad \lambda^{j_k} = 0, \qquad k = 1, \cdots, r - s,$$

in (1). Hence $C^s \subset A^r$ and the set C^s is determined in A^r by the system (6). Conversely, every system (6) determines some face of A^r. By Def. 4, every vertex of a simplex A^r is a 0-face of A^r, and A^r is its own r-face. Faces of dimension less than r are called *proper* faces of the simplex A^r.

D) The simplexes A and B of the Euclidean space R^n are said to be *properly situated* either if they are nonintersecting or if their intersection $A \cap B$ is a common face of A and B. If C is a face of the simplex A, and D is a face of the simplex B, with $A \cap B \subset C \cap D$, i.e., $A \cap B = C \cap D$, then clearly the simplexes A and B are properly situated if, and only if, the faces C and D are properly situated.

E) Two faces of a simplex are always properly situated.

Indeed, if C and D are two faces of the simplex A, then each of them is determined by a system of equations of the form (6). Two such systems of the form (6) combined again constitute either a system of the form (6) or an inconsistent system. The latter occurs if the joint system contains all the coordinates λ^i, in which case the intersection $C \cap D$ is empty; in the contrary case, this intersection is the common face of the simplexes C and D.

Complex

Let us turn now to the basic notion of a complex.

DEFINITION 5. A finite set K of simplexes of the Euclidean space R^n is called a *geometric complex*, or simply a *complex*, if K satisfies the following conditions:

1. If A is a simplex of K, then every face of A is also in K.
2. Every two simplexes of K are properly situated (see D)).

The 0-simplexes of a complex K are called its *vertices*.

The maximum dimension of the simplexes of K is called the *dimension* of K. An n-dimensional complex K will be referred to as an n-complex.

Although the complex is the fundamental notion of combinatorial topology, the real object of study turns out to be not the complex, but the topological space which is determined by it.

DEFINITION 6. Let K be a geometric complex situated in the Euclidean space R^n. The set of all points contained in the simplexes of the complex K is called a *polyhedron* and is denoted by $| K |$.

Since R^n is a metric space, $| K |$, as a subset of R^n, is also a metric space. The space $| K |$ is obviously compact, since it is the union of a finite number of compact sets, simplexes.

If K and L are two complexes and f is a continuous mapping of the polyhedron $| K |$ into the polyhedron $| L |$, then we shall sometimes refer to f as a mapping of the complex K into the complex L.

The simplest r-complex is the set T^r of all faces of the simplex A^r. The set S^{r-1} of all proper faces of the simplex A^r also forms a complex.

It is clear that $| T^r | = A^r$ and $| S^{r-1} | = F^{r-1}$, where F^{r-1} is the frontier of A^r (see A)).

In view of condition 1 of Def. 5, the vertices of each simplex of K are also vertices of K itself. Hence, in order to determine the complex K in R^n, it suffices to prescribe all the vertices of K and then to distinguish those sets of vertices whose spanning simplexes yield all the simplexes in K. Abstracting from the geometric positions of the vertices in R^n, we arrive at the notion of an abstract complex.

DEFINITION 7. A finite set $\mathfrak{K}$ of elements $\mathfrak{c}_0, \mathfrak{c}_1, \cdots, \mathfrak{c}_k$ is called an *abstract complex* with *vertices* $\mathfrak{c}_0, \mathfrak{c}_1, \cdots, \mathfrak{c}_k$ if $\mathfrak{K}$ satisfies the following conditions:

1. Certain non-empty subsets of the set $\mathfrak{K}$ are *distinguished* and are called *abstract simplexes* of the complex $\mathfrak{K}$.
2. Every subset of $\mathfrak{K}$ consisting of a single element is a distinguished subset. Hence every vertex of $\mathfrak{K}$ is also a simplex of $\mathfrak{K}$.
3. If $\mathfrak{A}$ is a simplex of $\mathfrak{K}$, then every non-empty subset of $\mathfrak{A}$, referred to as a *face* of the simplex $\mathfrak{A}$, is also a simplex of the complex $\mathfrak{K}$.

The abstract simplex $\mathfrak{A}^r = (\mathfrak{a}_0, \mathfrak{a}_1, \cdots, \mathfrak{a}_r)$ with $r + 1$ vertices is said to have *dimension* r. The maximum of the dimensions of the simplexes contained in the complex $\mathfrak{K}$ is called the *dimension* of the complex $\mathfrak{K}$. If the dimension of $\mathfrak{K}$ is n, $\mathfrak{K}$ will be referred to as an n-complex.

With every geometric complex K there is associated an abstract complex $\mathfrak{K}$, and conversely. The geometric complex K is called a *geometric realization* of the corresponding abstract complex $\mathfrak{K}$. The question as to whether every abstract complex admits of a geometric realization is treated in the following propositions.

Theorems of Realization

F) Let $\mathfrak{K}$ be an abstract complex with vertices $\mathfrak{c}_0, \mathfrak{c}_1, \cdots, \mathfrak{c}_k$, and $E^k = (e_0, e_1, \cdots, e_k)$ a k-simplex taken with its metric, $E^k \subset R^{k+1}$ (see B)). Let $\mathfrak{c}_{i_j} = \mathfrak{d}_j, j = 0, 1, \cdots, r$, denote any subset of $\mathfrak{c}_0, \mathfrak{c}_1, \cdots, \mathfrak{c}_k$ and let $e_{i_j} = v_j, j = 0, 1, \cdots, r$, denote the corresponding subset of $e_0, e_1, \cdots, e_k$. To each abstract simplex $\mathfrak{A}^r = (\mathfrak{d}_0, \mathfrak{d}_1, \cdots, \mathfrak{d}_r)$ of the complex $\mathfrak{K}$ assign the face $A^r = (v_0, v_1, \cdots, v_r)$ of the simplex E^k. The resulting set N of simplexes obviously forms a geometric complex, since the faces of the simplex E^k are properly situated (see E)). This geometric realization N will be referred to as the *natural realization* of the abstract complex $\mathfrak{K}$, and the metric of the polyhedron $|N|$ induced by the metric of E^k will be called the *natural metric* corresponding to $\mathfrak{K}$. The above yields a realization of $\mathfrak{K}$ in $E^k \subset R^{k+1}$. The point

$$\lambda^0 e_0 + \lambda^1 e_1 + \cdots + \lambda^k e_k = (\lambda^0, \lambda^1, \cdots, \lambda^k) = \lambda$$

(see B)) of the simplex E^k is obviously contained in the polyhedron $|N|$ if, and only if, $\lambda^{i_j} \neq 0, j = 0, 1, \cdots, r$, and the other coordinates zero implies that $\mathfrak{K}$ contains the simplex $(\mathfrak{d}_0, \mathfrak{d}_1, \cdots, \mathfrak{d}_r)$. Now let K be an arbitrary realization of the complex $\mathfrak{K}$ in the Euclidean space R^m. Denote the vertices of K by $c_0, c_1, \cdots, c_k$, where c_i corresponds to $\mathfrak{c}_i$. If to each point $\lambda = (\lambda^0, \lambda^1, \cdots, \lambda^k)$ of the polyhedron $|N|$ is assigned the point $\psi(\lambda) \in R^m$, where

$$\psi(\lambda) = \lambda^0 c_0 + \lambda^1 c_1 + \cdots + \lambda^k c_k,$$

then the resulting mapping ψ is a homeomorphism of $|N|$ onto $|K|$. Hence every realization of the complex $\mathfrak{K}$ is homeomorphic to the natural realization N of $\mathfrak{K}$, and therefore every two realizations of $\mathfrak{K}$ are homeomorphic.

Let us show that ψ is a homeomorphism of $|N|$ onto $|K|$. The mapping ψ is obviously continuous, and it suffices to prove that ψ is one-to-one and onto. This will establish that ψ is a homeomorphism, since $|N|$ is compact. To show that $\psi(|N|) = |K|$, let $A^r = (v_0, v_1, \cdots, v_r)$ be a simplex of N and $*A^r = (u_0, u_1, \cdots, u_r)$ the corresponding simplex in K, where $u_j = c_{i_j}, j = 0, 1, \cdots, r$. The mapping ψ of A^r into $*A^r$ is obviously onto and one-to-one. Since the existence of the simplex A^r in N implies the existence of the simplex $*A^r$ in K and conversely, it is clear that $\psi(|N|) = |K|$.

To show that $\psi(\lambda) = \psi(\mu)$ implies $\lambda = \mu$, let $\lambda = (\lambda^0, \lambda^1, \cdots, \lambda^k)$, $\mu = (\mu^0, \mu^1, \cdots, \mu^k)$ be two points of $|N|$, and denote by λ^{i_l}, $l = 0, 1, \cdots, r$, and μ^{j_p}, $p = 0, 1, \cdots, s$, those of the numbers λ^i and μ^j, respectively, which are different from zero. Let $e_{i_l} = t_l$, $l = 0, 1, \cdots, r$, and $e_{j_p} = w_p$, $p = 0, 1, \cdots, s$. If $A^r = (t_0, t_1, \cdots, t_r)$, $B^s = (w_0, w_1, \cdots, w_s)$, then the points λ and μ are interior points of A^r and B^s, respectively, which means that $\psi(\lambda)$ and $\psi(\mu)$ are interior points of $*A^r$ and $*B^s$, respectively. Since $*A^r$ and $*B^s$ are both in the same complex K, they are properly situated, and hence have a common interior point $\psi(\lambda) = \psi(\mu)$ only if they coincide. Hence $*A^r = *B^s$, which means that $A^r = B^s$. Since ψ is one-to-one on the simplex A^r, $\lambda = \mu$.

The dimension of the space R^{k+1} in which the natural realization N of the abstract complex $\mathfrak{K}$ is imbedded (see F)) depends on the number $k + 1$ of the vertices of $\mathfrak{K}$.

The following theorem gives a deeper result on the possibility of realizing an abstract complex.

THEOREM 3. *An abstract n-complex $\mathfrak{K}$ can always be realized by a geometric complex K imbedded in the Euclidean space R^{2n+1} of dimension $2n + 1$. To this end, the vertices of the complex K can be chosen arbitrarily, provided only that they be in general position* (see §1, Def. 2).

Proof. If $\mathfrak{c}_0, \mathfrak{c}_1, \cdots, \mathfrak{c}_k$ are the vertices of $\mathfrak{K}$, choose any system of points $c_0, c_1, \cdots, c_k$ in general position in R^{2n+1} (see Def. 2) and assign to $\mathfrak{c}_i$ the point c_i.

Now if $\mathfrak{A}^r = (\mathfrak{a}_0, \mathfrak{a}_1, \cdots, \mathfrak{a}_r)$ is any simplex of $\mathfrak{K}$, let $A^r = (a_0, a_1, \cdots, a_r)$ be the geometric simplex which spans the points $a_0, a_1, \cdots, a_r$ corresponding to the vertices $\mathfrak{a}_0, \mathfrak{a}_1, \cdots, \mathfrak{a}_r$. We must show that the resulting set K of simplexes of R^{2n+1} is a geometric complex, i.e., that K satisfies conditions 1 and 2 of Def. 5. Condition 1 follows immediately from condition 3 of Def. 7, and we now show that K satisfies condition 2.

Let $\mathfrak{A}^r$ and $\mathfrak{B}^s$ be two simplexes of $\mathfrak{K}$, A^r and B^s the corresponding geometric simplexes of K, and denote by $d_0, d_1, \cdots, d_t$ the set of all points which are vertices of at least one of the simplexes A^r and B^s. Since the dimension of $\mathfrak{K}$ is n, it follows that $r \leqq n$, $s \leqq n$, and therefore $t \leqq 2n + 1$. Hence $D^t = (d_0, d_1, \cdots, d_t)$ is a simplex in R^{2n+1}, which may or may not be in K. Since A^r and B^s are faces of D^t, they are properly situated (see E)). Hence K satisfies condition 2 of Def. 5 and is a complex. The geometric complex K obviously realizes $\mathfrak{K}$, and this proves the theorem.

We have therefore shown that with every abstract complex $\mathfrak{K}$ is associated a geometric complex K; and moreover, by the same token, that the polyhedron $|K|$ is determined uniquely, up to a homeomorphism, by the abstract complex $\mathfrak{K}$. The basic problem of combinatorial topology is the study of the topological properties of a polyhedron. In this respect, the complex plays a purely auxiliary role; it is used to determine the polyhedron and to construct its invariants. The customary way of constructing the invariants is to ascertain the properties of the abstract complex which determines the polyhedron, and then to prove that they are topological invariants of the latter.

§3. Application to dimension theory

This section is a digression in the direction of set-theoretic topology. Its content will be used very little in the sequel, except in §10, which is itself a digression from the basic theme of this book.

Dimension theory occupies a significant place in set-theoretic topology, deciding, as it does, the question as to what should be called the dimension, or the number of dimensions, of a topological space, and studying those properties of a topological space which have to do with its dimension. There are several different definitions of the dimension of a topological space, but for compact metric spaces the most important of these yield the same number. We shall give a definition of dimension only for compact metric spaces, and this definition will be phrased in terms of coverings of the space. The purpose of this section is to prove that every compact metric space of dimension r can be mapped homeomorphically onto some subset of the Euclidean space of dimension $2r + 1$. This result is one of the most basic in dimension theory, and is an excellent demonstration of the power of combinatorial methods in set-theoretic topology. Its proof is based on the notion of a nerve and on Theorem 4, both due to P. S. Alexandrov. The proof of this purely set-theoretic result rests on the use of basic elementary notions of combinatorial topology which, apparently, are indispensable here.

The Notions of Dimension and Nerve

A) Let R be a metric space, A a set of points in R, and δ a positive number. Denote by $H(A, \delta)$ the set of all points of R whose distance from A is less than δ, and by $\bar{H}(A, \delta)$ the set of all points of R whose distance from A does not exceed δ. It is clear that the closure of $H(A, \delta)$ is contained in $\bar{H}(A, \delta)$ and that $H(A, \delta)$ is open, while $\bar{H}(A, \delta)$ is closed. If A consists of one point a, the diameter of both sets $H(a, \delta)$ and $\bar{H}(a, \delta)$ evidently does not exceed 2δ.

B) Let R be a metric space, and denote by $\Sigma = \{C_0, C_1, \cdots, C_k\}$ a finite system of subsets of R. The system Σ is said to constitute a covering of the space R if each point of R is contained in at least one set of the system Σ. A covering Σ of the space R is called an ε-covering if the diameter of each set C_i of the system Σ is less than the positive number ε. It is customary to consider systems Σ consisting either entirely of open sets (open covering) or entirely of closed sets (closed covering). The system Σ of R is said to be of order n if there is a point of R which is contained in n sets of the system Σ, while no point of R is contained in $n + 1$ sets of Σ. We shall show that if R is a compact metric space and ε is a positive number, then R has both an open and a closed ε-covering.

In fact, $R = \bigcup_{x \epsilon r} H(x, \varepsilon/3)$ (see A)); and since R is compact, a finite number of these sets, say $H(x_0, \varepsilon/3), H(x_1, \varepsilon/3), \cdots, H(x_k, \varepsilon/3)$, will form an open ε-covering of R. As a closed ε-covering of R we may choose the system $\bar{H}(x_0, \varepsilon/3), \bar{H}(x_1, \varepsilon/3), \cdots, \bar{H}(x_k, \varepsilon/3)$.

Definition 8. The compact metric space R has a *finite dimension* r if both of the following conditions are satisfied:

1. For every positive ε there exists a closed ε-covering of R of order $\leqq r + 1$.

2. There exists a positive ε such that every closed ε-covering of R is of order $> r$.

If there is no integer $r \geqq 0$ which satisfies both of the above conditions, R is said to have infinite dimension. It is easily verified that the dimension of a space R is one of its topological invariants.

In fact, let R and R' be two compact metric spaces and f a homeomorphism of R onto R'. Since R is compact, f is uniformly continuous, and hence, for every positive number ε', there exists a positive number ε such that $\rho[f(x), f(y)] < \varepsilon'$ for $\rho(x, y) < \varepsilon$. If now $\Sigma = \{C_0, C_1, \cdots, C_k\}$ is a closed ε-covering of R, then the sets $f(C_i) = C'_i$, $i = 0, 1, \cdots, k$, form a closed ε'-covering Σ' of R'. Since f is one-to-one, Σ and Σ' are of the same order, and it follows immediately that the dimension of R' does not exceed the dimension of R. Since R and R' can be interchanged in the above argument, R and R' are of equal dimension.

We shall show in §10 that an r-simplex (see Def. 4) has dimension r in the sense of Def. 8 as well. There are also other reasons for considering Def. 8 to be appropriate.

C) If R is a compact metric space and $\Sigma = \{C_0, C_1, \cdots, C_k\}$ is a closed ε-covering of R, there exists a positive number δ (the Lebesgue number of the covering Σ) such that the closed covering $\bar{\Sigma}_\delta$ consisting of the sets $\bar{H}(C_i, \delta) = F_i$, $i = 0, 1, \cdots, k$ (see A)), is an ε-covering of the same order as the original covering Σ. This implies that the open covering Σ_δ consisting of the sets $H(C_i, \delta) = G_i$, $i = 0, 1, \cdots, k$, is an open ε-covering of the same order as Σ.

Let $C_{p_i} = \Gamma_i$, $i = 0, 1, \cdots, n$, be any system Σ' of sets whose intersection is empty, i.e., no point is contained in all the sets of the system Σ'. Setting $F_{p_i} = \Phi_i$, $i = 0, 1, \cdots, n$, we shall show that there is a positive η for which the intersection of the sets of the system $\bar{\Sigma}'_\eta = \{\Phi_0, \Phi_1, \cdots, \Phi_n\}$ is also empty. In the contrary case, there would exist, for each natural number m and $\eta = 1/m$, a point a_m contained in all the sets of the system $\bar{\Sigma}'_\eta$. Since R is compact, the sequence $a_1, a_2, \cdots, a_m, \cdots$ would have a limit point a; and since the sets of the system Σ' are closed, a would be contained in all the sets of the system Σ'.

Hence we may assign to each subsystem of the form Σ' of the system Σ a sufficiently small positive η for which the sets of the system $\bar{\Sigma}'_\eta$ have an empty intersection. Since Σ has only a finite number of subsets of the form Σ', we can take for δ the least of the numbers η, and this choice of δ will insure that the order of $\bar{\Sigma}_\delta$ is the same as that of Σ. Moreover, since the diameter of each of the sets C_i is less than ε, it is also possible to choose the above δ small enough so that the diameter of each of the sets F_i will be less than ε. The system $\bar{\Sigma}_\delta$ is then also an ε-covering. Proposition C) implies, in particular:

D) If the dimension of the compact metric space R is equal to r, then for every positive ε, there exists an open ε-covering of R whose order does not exceed $r + 1$.

DEFINITION 9. Let $\Sigma = \{C_0, C_1, \cdots, C_k\}$ be a system of sets of the space R. We shall construct the abstract complex $\mathfrak{K}$, called the *nerve* of the system Σ. With each set C_i associate the letter $\mathfrak{c}_i$ and take the set of letters $\mathfrak{c}_0, \mathfrak{c}_1, \cdots, \mathfrak{c}_k$ to be the set of vertices of the complex $\mathfrak{K}$. We shall regard the set of vertices $\mathfrak{c}_{i_j}$, $j = 0, 1, \cdots, s$, as defining a simplex of the complex $\mathfrak{K}$ if, and only if, the sets C_{i_j}, $j = 0, 1, \cdots, s$, have a non-empty intersection. If the system Σ is of order $r + 1$, then its nerve is obviously of dimension r.

E) A continuous mapping f of a metric space R into a metric space S is called an ε-mapping if the complete inverse image $f^{-1}(z)$ of every point $z \in f(R)$ is of diameter less than ε in R.

THEOREM 4. *Let R be a compact metric space, $\Sigma = \{G_0, G_1, \cdots, G_k\}$ an open ε-covering of R, $\mathfrak{K}$ the nerve of this covering, and K a geometric realization of $\mathfrak{K}$ in some Euclidean space R^m, so that to each set G_i of Σ there corresponds a point $c_i \in R^m$ which is a vertex of the geometric nerve K of the covering Σ. Then there exists a continuous ε-mapping f of the space R into the polyhedron $|K|$ for which $x \in G_p$ implies that $f(x)$ is contained in a simplex A^* of K with vertex c_p.*

Proof. Define the real-valued function $\varphi_i(x)$, $x \in R$, $i = 0, 1, \cdots, k$, as the distance of the point x to the closed set $R\backslash G_i$. The function $\varphi_i(x)$ is evidently continuous on R, is positive if and only if $x \in G_i$, and vanishes if $x \in R\backslash G_i$. Since every point x is contained in at least one of the sets G_i of the system Σ, the sum $\varphi(x) = \varphi_0(x) + \varphi_1(x) + \cdots + \varphi_k(x)$ is positive for every x. Setting $\lambda^i(x) = \varphi_i(x)/\varphi(x)$, we see that the function $\lambda^i(x)$ has the properties listed above for φ_i, and, moreover,

(1) $$\lambda^0(x) + \lambda^1(x) + \cdots + \lambda^k(x) = 1.$$

Let N be the natural realization of the abstract complex $\mathfrak{K}$ (see §2, F)), and assign to each point $x \in R$ the point

(2) $$\lambda(x) = \lambda^0(x)\, e_0 + \lambda^1(x)\, e_1 + \cdots + \lambda^k(x)\, e_k$$

of the Euclidean space R^{k+1}. Relation (1) and the nonnegativeness of $\lambda^i(x)$ imply that $\lambda(x)$ is contained in the simplex $E^k \subset R^{k+1}$. We shall show that $\lambda(x)$ is contained in the polyhedron $| N |$.

Let $x \in R$ and denote by $\Sigma_x = \{G_{i_j}, j = 0, 1, \cdots, r\}$ the set of all open sets of the system Σ which contain the point x. Since the open sets of the system Σ_x have a non-empty intersection, the simplex $\mathfrak{A} = (\mathfrak{c}_{i_0}, \mathfrak{c}_{i_1}, \cdots, \mathfrak{c}_{i_r})$ is in $\mathfrak{K}$, and hence the simplex $A = (e_{i_0}, e_{i_1}, \cdots, e_{i_r})$ is in N. On the other hand, λ^{i_j}, $j = 0, 1, \cdots, r$, are those numbers of the sequence $\lambda^0(x)$, $\lambda^1(x), \cdots, \lambda^k(x)$ which are different from zero, whence, by (2),

$$\lambda(x) = \textstyle\sum_{j=0}^{r} \lambda^{i_j} e_{i_j},$$

which means that $\lambda(x) \in A \in N$. Moreover, if $x \in G_p$, then G_p is a set of the system Σ_x and e_p is a vertex of the simplex A.

To show that the mapping λ of the space R into the polyhedron $| N |$ is an ε-mapping, let z be a point of $\lambda(R)$, $\lambda^{-1}(z)$ its complete inverse image in R, and $x \in \lambda^{-1}(z)$. Some set of the system Σ, say G_p, contains x, and hence $\lambda^p(x) \neq 0$. If now $y \in \lambda^{-1}(z)$, then $\lambda(x) = \lambda(y)$, and, by (2), $\lambda^p(y) = \lambda^p(x) \neq 0$. Therefore $y \in G_p$, i.e., $\lambda^{-1}(z) \subset G_p$; and since the diameter of G_p is less than ε and $\lambda^{-1}(z) \subset G_p$, the diameter of $\lambda^{-1}(z)$ is also less than ε.

We shall now make the transition from the complex N to the complex K by means of the mapping ψ (see §2, F)) by setting $f(x) = \psi[\lambda(x)]$. Since ψ is a homeomorphism of N onto K and maps each simplex of N onto a corresponding simplex of K, f satisfies the requirements of the theorem. Explicitly, the mapping of R into $| K |$ is given by

(3) $$f(x) = \lambda^0(x)c_0 + \lambda^1(x)c_1 + \cdots + \lambda^k(x)c_k.$$

This proves the theorem.

If the space R has dimension r, then, by D), for every positive ε there exists an open ε-covering Σ of R whose order does not exceed $r + 1$. Hence there is a continuous ε-mapping f of the space R into the r-dimensional polyhedron $| K |$, the nerve of the covering Σ. This result establishes a very important connection between general compact metric spaces and polyhedra; it is due to P. S. Alexandrov and has numerous applications in topology.

The Space of Mappings and the Imbedding Theorem

F) Let R be a metric space. A sequence $a_0, a_1, \cdots, a_m, \cdots$ of points of R is called a Cauchy sequence, if for every positive ε there exists a natural number n such that $\rho(a_p, a_q) < \varepsilon$ for $p > n, q > n$. It is easily shown that a Cauchy sequence can have but one limit point, and if a Cauchy sequence does have a limit point, then it converges to that point. The space R is called complete if every Cauchy sequence in R converges. It is easily seen that a compact space is always complete, just as a Euclidean space is complete. If $G_0 = R, G_1, \cdots, G_m, \cdots$ is a sequence of open sets of a complete metric space, each of which is everywhere dense in R, then the intersection of all these open sets is non-vacuous and even everywhere dense in R.

To prove the last statement, let a_0 be any point of $G_0 = R$ and let ε_0 be any positive number. We shall show that there is a point a contained in all the sets G_m such that $\rho(a_0, a) \leqq \varepsilon_0$.

Suppose that the finite sequence of points $a_0, a_1, \cdots, a_n$ of the space R and the finite sequence of numbers $\varepsilon_0, \varepsilon_1 < 1, \cdots, \varepsilon_n < 1/n$ have already been constructed so as to satisfy the conditions

$$(4) \qquad \bar{H}(a_i, \varepsilon_i) \subset H(a_{i-1}, \varepsilon_{i-1}) \cap G_i, \qquad i = 1, 2, \cdots, n \qquad \text{(see A)).}$$

We shall extend these two sequences. Since G_{n+1} is everywhere dense in R, there exists a point $a_{n+1} \in H(a_n, \varepsilon_n) \cap G_{n+1}$; and since $H(a_n, \varepsilon_n) \cap G_{n+1}$ is an open set, there exists a positive number $\varepsilon_{n+1} < 1/(n+1)$ such that $\bar{H}(a_{n+1}, \varepsilon_{n+1}) \subset H(a_n, \varepsilon_n) \cap G_{n+1}$. Hence the sequences $a_0, a_1, \cdots, a_m, \cdots$ and $\varepsilon_0, \varepsilon_1, \cdots, \varepsilon_m, \cdots$ are infinite and satisfy condition (4). If $p < q$, then $a_q \in H(a_p, \varepsilon_p)$, whence $\rho(a_p, a_q) < \varepsilon_p < 1/p$. Thus $a_0, a_1, \cdots, a_m, \cdots$ is a Cauchy sequence, and therefore converges to some point a. The sequence $a_m, a_{m+1}, \cdots$ also converges to the same point a, and is contained in the closed set $\bar{H}(a_m, \varepsilon_m)$. Therefore $a \in \bar{H}(a_m, \varepsilon_m)$ and a is contained in all the sets G_m. Moreover, $\rho(a_0, a) \leqq \varepsilon_0$, since $a \in \bar{H}(a_0, \varepsilon_0)$. This proves the assertion.

Definition 10. Let R be a compact metric space, S an arbitrary metric space, and Φ the set of all continuous mappings of the space R into the space S. If f and g are two mappings of Φ, then $\rho[f(x), g(x)]$ is a continuous real-valued function defined on the compact space R, and therefore attains its maximum; we define this maximum, denoted by $\rho(f, g)$, to be the distance between the elements f and g in the metric space just defined. It will be shown below that $\rho(f, g)$ satisfies all the axioms of a metric space. We shall also show that if S is complete, then Φ is complete.

It is clear that $\rho(f, g) = 0$ if, and only if, $f = g$. Similarly, it is obvious that $\rho(f, g) = \rho(g, f)$. To prove the triangle inequality, i.e., if $f, g, h \in \Phi$, then $\rho(f, h) \leqq \rho(f, g) + \rho(g, h)$, let a be a point of R for which $\rho[f(x), h(x)]$ attains its maximum. Then

$$\rho(f, h) = \rho[f(a), h(a)] \leqq \rho[f(a), g(a)] + \rho[g(a), h(a)] \leqq \rho(f, g) + \rho(g, h).$$

This proves that the metric axioms are satisfied for Φ.

Let us now show that if S is complete, then Φ is also complete. If f_0, $f_1, \cdots, f_m, \cdots$ is a Cauchy sequence of Φ, then for every positive ε there exists a natural number n such that $\rho(f_p, f_q) < \varepsilon$ for $p > n$, $q > n$. Hence,

$$\rho[f_p(x), f_q(x)] < \varepsilon \tag{5}$$

for any point $x \in R$. Thus $f_0(x), f_1(x), \cdots, f_m(x), \cdots$ is a Cauchy sequence of S, and therefore converges to a point of S which we denote by $f(x)$. Letting $q \to \infty$ in (5), we get

$$\rho[f_p(x), f(x)] \leqq \varepsilon \tag{6}$$

for $p > n$.

We shall show now that f is a continuous mapping of R into S. Since f_p is continuous at x, there exists a positive δ such that $\rho[f_p(x), f_p(y)] < \varepsilon$ for $\rho(x, y) < \delta$. Since relation (6) holds also for the point y, we have

$$\rho[f(x), f(y)] \leqq \rho[f(x), f_p(x)] + \rho[f_p(x), f_p(y)] + \rho[f_p(y), f(y)] < 3\,\varepsilon.$$

Hence f is a continuous mapping, i.e., $f \in \Phi$. Moreover, since relation (6) implies that $\rho(f_p, f) \leqq \varepsilon$ for $p > n$, the sequence $f_0, f_1, \cdots, f_m, \cdots$ converges to f.

G) If Φ is the metric space of all continuous mappings of a compact metric space R into an arbitrary metric space S (see Def. 10), and Φ_ε is the set of all ε-mappings of Φ (see E)), then Φ_ε is an open set in Φ.

If $f \in \Phi_\varepsilon$, then there exists a positive number δ such that $x, y \in R$ and $\rho[f(x), f(y)] < \delta$ imply $\rho(x, y) < \varepsilon$. In the contrary case, there is a sequence $\delta_1, \delta_2, \cdots, \delta_m, \cdots$ of positive numbers tending to zero, and a pair of points x_m, y_m for each natural number m, such that $\rho[f(x_m), f(y_m)] < \delta_m$ and $\rho(x_m, y_m) \geqq \varepsilon$. Since R is compact, we can choose a convergent subsequence from the sequence $x_1, x_2, \cdots, x_m, \cdots$. In order not to change the notation, suppose that the sequence $x_1, x_2, \cdots, x_m, \cdots$ itself converges to a point x. Similarly, we can suppose that the sequence $y_1, y_2, \cdots, y_m, \cdots$ converges to a point y. Then $\rho[f(x), f(y)] = 0$, i.e., $f(x) = f(y)$, while $\rho(x, y) \geqq \varepsilon$, which contradicts the assumption that f is an ε-mapping.

We shall now show that $\rho(f, g) < \delta/2$ implies that g is an ε-mapping, i.e., Φ_ε is an open set. If $g(x) = g(y) = z$, then

$$\rho[f(x), f(y)] \leqq \rho[f(x), g(x)] + \rho[g(y), f(y)] < (\delta/2) + (\delta/2) = \delta,$$

whence $\rho(x, y) < \varepsilon$. Since the complete inverse image $\overset{-1}{g}(z)$ of the point

$z \in g(R)$ is compact in R and $\rho(x, y) < \varepsilon$ for $x, y \in g^{-1}(z)$, the diameter of $g^{-1}(z)$ must be less than ε. Hence $g \in \Phi_\varepsilon$, and proposition G) is proved.

THEOREM 5. *A compact metric space R of dimension r can be mapped homeomorphically onto some subset of the Euclidean space R^{2r+1} of dimension $2r + 1$.*

Proof. Let Φ be the space of all continuous mappings of the space R into the space R^{2r+1} (see Def. 10), and denote by Φ_ε the set of all ε-mappings of Φ. In virtue of G), Φ_ε is open in Φ. It is clear that $\Phi_1, \Phi_{1/2}, \cdots, \Phi_{1/m}, \cdots$ is a decreasing sequence of open sets of Φ. Denote the intersection of all the open sets $\Phi_{1/m}$ by Ψ. Since each $h \in \Psi$ is an ε-mapping for every $\varepsilon > 0$, h is a one-to-one, continuous mapping of the space R onto the subset $h(R)$ of R^{2r+1}, and h is a homeomorphism, because R is compact. Hence it suffices to prove that Ψ is non-vacuous. By F), this will follow if it is shown that Φ_ε is everywhere dense in Φ. Let us prove this fact.

We shall show that if $g \in \Phi$ and ε, η are any two positive numbers, then there exists an ε-mapping f of R into R^{2r+1} such that $\rho(g, f) < \eta$. This will prove that Φ_ε is everywhere dense in Φ. Since g is uniformly continuous, there is a positive $\delta \leqq \varepsilon$ such that $\rho(x, y) < \delta$ implies $\rho[g(x), g(y)] < \eta/6$. Now let $\Sigma = \{G_0, G_1, \cdots, G_k\}$ be an open δ-covering of R whose order does not exceed $r + 1$ (see D)). Since $\delta \leqq \varepsilon$, Σ is also an ε-covering. Since the diameter of each set G_i is less than δ, the diameter of each set $g(G_i) = F_i$ is less than $\eta/6$. Choose points c_i, $i = 0, 1, \cdots, k$, of R^{2r+1} so that the distance of c_i from F_i is less than $\eta/6$ and such that $c_0, c_1, \cdots, c_k$ are in general position (this choice is possible by Theorem 2). Take the points c_0, $c_1, \cdots, c_k$ as the vertices of the geometric nerve K (see Theorem 3) of the covering Σ, and associate with the vertex c_i the element G_i of the covering Σ. We shall show that the mapping f of the space R into the nerve K, constructed in Theorem 4, satisfies the requirements of the present theorem.

Since Σ is an open ε-covering, f is an ε-mapping by Theorem 4. It remains to be shown that $\rho(g, f) < \eta$.

Let us estimate, first, the diameters of the simplexes of the complex K by means of proposition C) of §9, whose proof depends only on the definition of a simplex. This proposition asserts that the diameter of a simplex is equal to the length of its longest edge, i.e., one-dimensional face. Hence it suffices to estimate only the diameters of the 1-simplexes of K. If (c_p, c_q) is any 1-simplex of K, the sets G_p and G_q have a common point, whence the sets F_p and F_q have a non-empty intersection. Since the diameter of each of the sets F_p and F_q is less than $\eta/6$, and the distances of the points c_p and c_q to the sets F_p and F_q, respectively, are also less than $\eta/6$, it follows that $\rho(c_p, c_q) < \frac{2}{3}\eta$. Hence the diameter of every simplex of K is less than $\frac{2}{3}\eta$.

Now, if x is any point of R, there is an open set G_p of the system Σ which contains x. Since $g(x) \in F_p$ and the distance of the vertex c_p from the set F_p is less than $\eta/6$, it follows that $\rho[g(x), c_p] < \eta/3$. On the other hand, by

Theorem 4, the point $f(x)$ is contained in the simplex A^* of K with vertex c_p; and since the diameter of A^* is less than $\frac{2}{3}\eta$, $\rho[c_p, f(x)] < \frac{2}{3}\eta$. Hence $\rho[g(x), f(x)] < \eta$, and since x is any point of R, $\rho(g, f) < \eta$. This proves Theorem 5.

As a supplement to Theorem 5, we remark that for every natural number r there exists an r-dimensional compact metric space P^r which cannot be mapped homeomorphically onto a subset of the Euclidean space R^{2r} of dimension $2r$. This very non-trivial result is due to van Kampen, who defined the space P^r in the following way. If A^{2r+2} is a $(2r + 2)$-simplex, the set of all faces of A^{2r+2} whose dimension does not exceed r forms an r-complex K^r. The space P^r is the polyhedron $|K^r|$. If $r = 1$, the complex K^1 can be easily imagined, and it is not difficult to prove by elementary methods that $|K^1|$ cannot be mapped homeomorphically onto a subset of the plane. If $r > 1$, the proof depends on the notion of intersection number, which is not considered in this book.

§4. The Betti groups

We shall apply here the general method of constructing the invariants of a polyhedron, mentioned at the end of §2, to the determination of the basic invariants, the Betti groups. A proof of the invariance of the Betti groups will be given in Chapter II. Since the definition and analysis of the Betti groups in this and later sections of the present chapter depend on a complex only in the sense of its combinatorial scheme, there is no need here to distinguish between an abstract complex and its geometric realization.

A) An arbitrary order of succession $a, b, c, \cdots, f$ of the set of all vertices of a simplex will be called a vertex ordering of this simplex. The simplex $(a_0, a_1, \cdots, a_r)$ is said to receive an *orientation* or to be *oriented*, if each of its vertex orderings is assigned the sign $+$ or $-$ in such a way, that orderings differing by an odd permutation receive opposite signs. This can be written in the form

$$A^r = \varepsilon\, (a_0, a_1, \cdots, a_r), \tag{1}$$

where ε denotes that sign which is assigned to the ordering $a_0, a_1, \cdots, a_r$, $\varepsilon = \pm 1$. Hence every simplex receives two different (opposite) orientations. If A^r is an oriented simplex, $-A^r$ will denote the oppositely oriented simplex.

Although a 0-simplex (a_0) has only one vertex ordering, it shall nevertheless be assigned, by definition, two opposite orientations, $+(a_0)$ and $-(a_0)$.

B) If $(a_0, a_1, \cdots, a_r)$ is an r-simplex, any one of its $(r - 1)$-faces can be obtained by canceling one vertex a_i from the sequence $a_0, a_1, \cdots, a_r$. The resulting face will be referred to as the face opposite the vertex a_i.

With the orientation $A^r = \varepsilon\,(a_0, a_1, \cdots, a_r)$ of the original simplex associate the orientation

$$B_i^{r-1} = (-1)^i\,\varepsilon\,(a_0, a_1, \cdots, a_{i-1}, a_{i+1}, \cdots, a_r)$$

of the $(r-1)$-face of A^r opposite the vertex a_i. It is easily verified that this correspondence between the orientations of A^r and B_i^{r-1} is independent of the vertex ordering $a_0, a_1, \cdots, a_r$. If A^r corresponds to B_i^{r-1}, then obviously $-A^r$ corresponds to $-B_i^{r-1}$. The simplexes A^r and B_i^{r-1} are said to be *coherently* oriented.

C) Let $A^r{}_1, A^r{}_2, \cdots, A^r{}_{\alpha(r)}$ be the set of all arbitrarily oriented r-simplexes of a complex K, and G an arbitrary commutative group taken in the additive notation. The linear form

$$x = g_1 A^r{}_1 + g_2 A^r{}_2 + \cdots + g_{\alpha(r)} A^r{}_{\alpha(r)} \tag{2}$$

in the simplexes $A^r{}_1, A^r{}_2, \cdots, A^r{}_{\alpha(r)}$ with coefficients $g_1, g_2, \cdots, g_{\alpha(r)}$ in G, is called an r-dimensional *chain*, or simply an r-chain, of the complex K over (the coefficient group) G. If $*A^r{}_1, *A^r{}_2, \cdots, *A^r{}_{\alpha(r)}$ are the r-simplexes of K taken with any other orientations, $*A^r{}_i = \varepsilon_i A^r{}_i$, we shall write

$$x = \varepsilon_1 g_1\, *A^r{}_1 + \varepsilon_2 g_2\, *A^r{}_2 + \cdots + \varepsilon_{\alpha(r)} g_{\alpha(r)}\, *A^r{}_{\alpha(r)}\,.$$

This makes the definition of a chain independent of the choice of orientation of the simplexes. If

$$x = \sum_{i=1}^{\alpha(r)} g_i A^r{}_i\,, \qquad y = \sum_{i=1}^{\alpha(r)} h_i A^r{}_i$$

are two r-chains of K over G, set

$$x + y = \sum_{i=1}^{\alpha(r)} (g_i + h_i) A^r{}_i\,. \tag{3}$$

This defines the operation of addition in the set of all r-chains of K over G, and the set becomes a commutative group, which will be denoted by $L^r(K, G)$, or simply by L^r, when this cannot lead to misunderstanding.

The group G used in the formation of chains is in most cases taken to be either the group G_0 of integers or the group G_m of residues modulo m. For brevity we shall write $L^r(K, G_m) = L^r{}_m$, $m = 0, 1, 2, \cdots$. Especially useful are the groups G_0 and G_2. The use of G_2 enables us to dispense with oriented simplexes, since in this case $g = -g$ and there is no need to distinguish between the simplex A^r and the simplex $-A^r$ in the chain x.

Definition 11. If A^r is an oriented r-simplex of a complex K, it can be regarded as a chain of K over G_0 (the group of integers). The *boundary of the oriented simplex* A^r is defined as the $(r-1)$-chain of K over G_0 given by

$$\Delta(A^r) = \Delta A^r = B_0^{r-1} + B_1^{r-1} + \cdots + B_r^{r-1}, \tag{4}$$

where $B_0^{r-1}, B_1^{r-1}, \cdots, B_r^{r-1}$ is the set of all $(r-1)$-faces of A^r coherently oriented with respect to A^r. If $r = 0$, set

$$\Delta A^0 = 0. \tag{4'}$$

It is clear that

$$\Delta(-A^r) = -\Delta(A^r).$$

The definition of boundary is extended to an arbitrary r-chain x of K over G (see (2)) by setting

$$\Delta(x) = \Delta x = \sum_{i=1}^{\alpha(r)} g_i \Delta A^r{}_i . \tag{5}$$

It is easy to see that

$$\Delta(-x) = -\Delta x \quad \text{and} \quad \Delta(x + y) = \Delta(x) + \Delta(y). \tag{6}$$

We shall show, moreover, that

$$\Delta\Delta x = 0. \tag{7}$$

It suffices to prove (7) for the case $x = A^r$. Let $A^r = +(a_0, a_1, \cdots, a_r)$ and let C_p^{r-1}, C_{pq}^{r-2} be the oriented simplexes obtained from A^r by omitting, respectively, the vertex a_p and the two vertices a_p and a_q, $p < q$, i.e.,

$$C_p^{r-1} = +(a_0, a_1, \cdots, a_{p-1}, a_{p+1}, \cdots, a_r),$$
$$C_{pq}^{r-2} = +(a_0, a_1, \cdots, a_{p-1}, a_{p+1}, \cdots, a_{q-1}, a_{q+1}, \cdots, a_r).$$

Then,

$$\Delta A^r = \sum_{i=0}^{r} (-1)^i C_i^{r-1}$$

and

$$\Delta C_i^{r-1} = \sum_{j=0}^{i-1} (-1)^j C_{ji}^{r-2} + \sum_{j=i+1}^{r} (-1)^{j-1} C_{ij}^{r-2}.$$

Hence

$$\Delta\Delta A^r = \Sigma_{j<i} (-1)^{i+j} C_{ji}^{r-2} + \Sigma_{i<j} (-1)^{j+i-1} C_{ij}^{r-2} = 0,$$

which proves (7).

The boundary operator Δ is the most important in combinatorial topology, and leads to the following basic notions of the so-called homology theory.

Definition 12. An r-chain x is called a *cycle* if its boundary is equal to zero, i.e., if $\Delta x = 0$. The set of all r-cycles of K over G is denoted by $Z^r(K, G)$, or simply by Z^r [$Z^r(K, G_m) = Z^r{}_m$]. The set Z^r is clearly a subgroup of the group L^r (see (6)) and, in particular, if $r = 0$, $Z^0 = L^0$ (see (4')).

We note that every boundary is a cycle (see (7)).

Definition 13. An r-cycle z of an n-complex K is said to be *homologous to zero* if it is the boundary of an $(r + 1)$-chain of K, $r = 0, 1, 2, \cdots, n - 1$. An n-cycle z is considered homologous to zero only if it is equal to zero. In symbols, "z homologous to zero" is written as "$z \sim 0$". The set of all r-cycles of K over G which are homologous to zero is denoted by $H^r(K, G)$, or simply by H^r $[H^r(K, G_m) = H^r{}_m]$. It is clear that H^r is a subgroup of the group Z^r (see (7)). Two r-cycles z_1 and z_2 are said to be *homologous* ($z_1 \sim z_2$) if their difference is homologous to zero ($z_1 - z_2 \sim 0$).

DEFINITION 14. Since $H^r \subset Z^r$ (see Defs. 12, 13), we can form the factor group $B^r = Z^r/H^r$. The group $B^r = B^r(K, G)$ is called the r-dimensional *Betti group* or the r-dimensional *homology group* of the complex K over G $[B^r(K, G_m) = B^r{}_m]$.

The elements of the Betti group, in virtue of Defs. 13 and 14, are classes or cosets of homologous cycles. The definition of the terms "cycle" and "homologous to zero" depends of course on the group G used in the basic construction.

It turns out that in order to determine the Betti groups of a complex K over an arbitrary group G, it suffices to know the Betti groups over the group of integers G_0; because of this, the group G_0 plays a particularly important role. However, we shall not prove this fact.

It will be proved in the sequel that the Betti groups of a complex K are topological invariants of the corresponding polyhedron $|K|$. The Betti groups of a polyhedron are the basic topological invariants, and have been studied more thoroughly than any of the others.

D) If K is an n-complex and Δ is the boundary operator in K, then Δ is a homomorphism of the group L^r into the group L^{r-1} (see (6)), $r = 1, 2, \cdots, n$. In virtue of Defs. 12 and 13, the subgroup Z^r is the kernel of the homomorphism Δ in the group L^r, and the subgroup $H^{r-1} \subset L^{r-1}$ is the image of L^r under Δ. Hence the groups L^r/Z^r and H^{r-1} are isomorphic.

E) If x^*, y^*, z^* are elements of the Betti group B^r of a complex K, and x, y, z are cycles of K in the corresponding homology classes x^*, y^*, z^*, then the relations $x^* + y^* = z^*$ and $x + y \sim z$ are equivalent. Hence an arbitrary relation between the elements of the Betti group B^r can be replaced by a relation between cycles by using the homology symbol in place of the equality sign. Therefore, in studying homology relations between cycles, we study, by the same token, properties of Betti groups, and this is the significance of the homology symbol. To give an example, the notion of linear independence of the elements of a Betti group can be replaced by the notion of independence of cycles with respect to homology.

§5. Decomposition into components. The zero-dimensional Betti group

This section is devoted to the clarification of the geometrical meaning of the zero-dimensional Betti group of a complex. As a preliminary to this, we shall prove a general proposition, which is also of some independent interest (see Theorem 6).

A) A *subcomplex* of a complex K is any complex L all of whose simplexes are contained in K. The set of all simplexes of a complex K, whose dimension does not exceed r, is called the r-dimensional *skeleton*, or simply the r-*skeleton*, of the complex K. The r-skeleton of K is a subcomplex of K.

B) A complex K is said to be *connected* if it cannot be represented as the union of two non-empty subcomplexes L and M without common simplexes. A complex is connected if, and only if, given any two of its vertices a and e, there exists a sequence of vertices

$$a_1 = a, a_2, \cdots, a_q = e \tag{1}$$

such that a_i, a_{i+1}, $i = 1, 2, \cdots, q - 1$, are the vertices of a 1-simplex of K.

To prove this, suppose first that the complex K is not connected, i.e., is the union of two disjoint non-vacuous subcomplexes L and M. Let a be a vertex of L and e a vertex of M, and assume that a sequence (1) exists for these vertices. If a_i is the last vertex of (1) which is contained in L, the simplex (a_i, a_{i+1}), which exists according to the above condition, cannot lie in either L or M. Hence, if K is not connected, the sequence (1) is lacking for at least one pair of vertices of K.

Assume now that the complex K is connected. Let a be a fixed, but arbitrary, vertex of K and denote by E the set of all vertices e of K which can be joined to a by a sequence of the form (1). If a simplex A has at least one vertex in E, then obviously all its vertices are in E. Hence the set of all simplexes of K with vertices in E forms a subcomplex L of K. The set of all simplexes of K which are not in L clearly also forms a subcomplex M of K, which, however, is empty since K is connected. Therefore E contains all the vertices of K, and the fixed vertex a can be joined to an arbitrary vertex e by a sequence of the form (1). This immediately implies that every pair of vertices of K can be joined by a sequence (1).

C) Any connected subcomplex L of the complex K, such that K is the union of two disjoint complexes L and M, will be called a *component* of K. If $K_1, \cdots, K_p$ is the set of all components of K, then $K_i \cap K_j = 0$, $i \neq j$, and K is the union of the complexes $K_1, \cdots, K_p$.

Assume that the components K_i and K_j intersect. Since K_i is a component, K is the union of two disjoint subcomplexes $K_i = L$ and M. Denoting the intersections of K_j with L and M by K'_j and K''_j, respectively, it is easily seen that K'_j and K''_j are disjoint subcomplexes of the complex K_j, and that their union is K_j. Since K_j is connected, one of the subcomplexes K'_j or K''_j, in fact the latter, must be empty, because

$K'_j = K_i \cap K_j$, which is non-empty by hypothesis. Hence $K_j \subset K_i$. Similarly, it can be shown that $K_i \subset K_j$, i.e., $K_i = K_j$, whence $i = j$.

We shall prove now that K is the union of all its components, by showing that an arbitrary simplex A of K is contained in one of the components. If K is connected, there is exactly one component, $K = K_1$, and the assertion is true. If K is not connected, it is the union of two disjoint subcomplexes L and M, and one of these, say L, contains A. If L is connected, then L is a component of K, and the simplex A is contained in one of the components of K. If L is not connected, we extend the decomposition until a component containing A is reached.

A fixed coefficient group G is used in what follows, and this fact will not be mentioned explicitly again.

THEOREM 6. *If $K_1, \cdots, K_p$ is the set of all components of a complex K, and B^r, B^r_i are the Betti groups of the complexes K and K_i, respectively, then B^r is isomorphic to the direct sum $B^r_1 + \cdots + B^r_p$.*

Proof. Let L^r be the group of all r-chains of the complex K, and denote by L^r_i that subgroup of L^r which consists of all chains of L^r in which the only simplexes appearing with non-vanishing coefficients are simplexes of the complex K_i. It is clear that

$$L^r = L^r_1 + \cdots + L^r_p, \tag{2}$$

and that L^r_i is the group of all r-chains of the complex K_i. Furthermore, if we set $H_i^{r-1} = \Delta L^r_i$, then

$$H_i^{r-1} \subset L_i^{r-1}. \tag{3}$$

We shall show that

$$H^{r-1} = H_1^{r-1} + \cdots + H_p^{r-1}. \tag{4}$$

Indeed, if Δx, where $x \in L^r$, is any element of H^{r-1}, then, by (2),

$$x = x_1 + \cdots + x_p, \qquad x_i \in L^r_i,$$

and hence

$$\Delta x = \Delta x_1 + \cdots + \Delta x_p, \tag{5}$$

where $\Delta x_i \in H_i^{r-1}$. The uniqueness of the decomposition (5) follows from (2) and (3).

Denoting by Z^r_i the kernel of the homomorphism Δ in the group L^r_i, it will be shown that

$$Z^r = Z^r_1 + \cdots + Z^r_p. \tag{6}$$

If $z \in Z^r$, then $z = x_1 + \cdots + x_p$, where $x_i \in L^r_i$ (see (2)). Hence

$$\Delta x_1 + \cdots + \Delta x_p = \Delta z = 0;$$

and by (3) and (4), this yields $\Delta x_i = 0$, so that $x_i \in Z^r{}_i$. The uniqueness of this decomposition of z follows from (2).

Relations (4) and (6) imply that the group Z^r/H^r is isomorphic to the direct sum $Z^r{}_1/H^r{}_1 + \cdots + Z^r{}_p/H^r{}_p$. This proves Theorem 6.

D) Let K be an arbitrary complex, and $A^0{}_1, \cdots, A^0{}_\alpha$ the set of all positively oriented 0-simplexes $A^0{}_i = +(a_i)$ of K. If

$$x = g_1A^0{}_1 + g_2A^0{}_2 + \cdots + g_\alpha A^0{}_\alpha$$

is any 0-chain of K over G, define the Kronecker index $I(x)$ of the chain x by setting

$$I(x) = g_1 + \cdots + g_\alpha .$$

It is clear that

$$I(x + y) = I(x) + I(y). \tag{7}$$

We shall show that $x \sim 0$ implies $I(x) = 0$.

Let $A^1 = +(a, b)$ be any oriented 1-simplex of K, and set

$$A^0 = +(a), \qquad B^0 = +(b).$$

Then $\Delta(gA^1) = gB^0 - gA^0$, which implies that $I[\Delta(gA^1)] = 0$, which in turn, by (7), implies that $I(\Delta y) = 0$ for any $y \in L^1$. This proves the assertion.

We remark that it is not possible to introduce the notion of index for chains whose dimension is greater than zero. Indeed, only in the case of a 0-simplex can we speak of a positive orientation, since only then does there exist a unique vertex ordering.

E) If K is a connected complex, then $I(x) = 0$ is equivalent to $x \sim 0$; and moreover, $B^0(K, G)$ is isomorphic to G.

Let a and e be any two vertices of K, and set $A^0 = +(a)$, $E^0 = +(e)$. Since K is connected, there exists a sequence (1) such that K contains the simplexes (a_i, a_{i+1}), $i = 1, \cdots, q - 1$. Setting $A^1{}_i = +(a_i, a_{i+1})$, the boundary of the chain

$$y = gA^1{}_1 + gA^1{}_2 + \cdots + gA^1{}_{q-1}$$

over G is obviously $\Delta y = gE^0 - gA^0$. Hence $gE^0 \sim gA^0$, and this immediately implies that any 0-chain x over an arbitrary group G is homologous to a chain gA^0, $g \in G$. Since x and gA^0 are homologous, their indices are equal, and hence $I(x) = g$. Therefore

$$x \sim I(x)A^0.$$

The last relation shows that if $I(x) = 0$, then $x \sim 0$, which proves that the relations $I(x) = 0$ and $x \sim 0$ are equivalent.

By (7), the operator I is a homomorphic mapping of the group $L^0 = Z^0$ into the group G. If $g \in G$, there is a cycle gA^0 in Z^0 whose Kronecker index is equal to g, and hence $I(Z^0) = G$. On the other hand, the equivalence of the relations $I(x) = 0$ and $x \sim 0$ implies that H^0 is the kernel of the homomorphism I. Hence Z^0/H^0 is isomorphic to G, and this completes the proof of proposition E).

THEOREM 7. *The zero-dimensional Betti group of an arbitrary complex K over G is isomorphic to the direct sum $G + \cdots + G$, where the number of terms in the direct sum is the same as the number of components of the complex K.*

This theorem follows immediately from Theorem 6 and proposition E).

§6. The Betti numbers. The Euler-Poincaré formula

Since the Betti group B^r of a complex K is a topological invariant of the polyhedron $|K|$, any numerical invariant of the Betti group is an invariant of $|K|$. Particularly great interest attaches, of course, to finding a complete system of numerical invariants of the Betti group. The problem of constructing a complete system of numerical invariants will be solved here for the Betti group $B^r{}_0$ over G_0, the group of integers, and also for the Betti group $B^r{}_m$ over G_m, the group of residues modulo m, m a prime. A complete system of invariants for the group $B^r{}_0$ consists of its rank, which is the Betti number, and its torsion coefficients. The group $B^r{}_m$ has just one invariant, the Betti number modulo m. In this section we shall also derive the Euler-Poincaré formula, which gives two expressions for the Euler characteristic of a complex: one in terms of the Betti numbers, i.e., invariant expressions, and the other in terms of the number of simplexes of different dimensions, which are non-invariant expressions.

Let us first recall several fundamental facts of the theory of commutative groups. The groups will be written additively.

A) The commutative group A is said to admit of a *finite system of generators* $x_1, \cdots, x_s$, $x_i \in A$, if every $x \in A$ is of the form

$$x = \lambda_1 x_1 + \cdots + \lambda_s x_s,$$

where $\lambda_1, \cdots, \lambda_s$ are integers. It is known that every factor group and every subgroup of a group with a finite system of generators also admits of a finite system of generators. A group A generated by a single element x_1 is called a *cyclic* group. If the relation $\lambda x_1 = 0$, where λ is an integer, implies $\lambda = 0$, the generator x_1 and the group A itself are called *free* or of *order zero*. If there exists a natural number λ such that $\lambda x_1 = 0$ and λ is the least natural number satisfying this condition, then the generator x_1 and the group A itself are said to be of *finite order* λ.

B) Every commutative group A with a finite system of generators is a direct sum of cyclic groups

$$A_1, \cdots, A_r; \qquad B_1, \cdots, B_q,$$

where the A_i's are free cyclic groups and each B_j is a cyclic group of finite order τ_j, with τ_{j+1} divisible by τ_j. [For a proof of this fact, see Pontryagin, *Topological Groups*, Ch. I.] The numbers $r, \tau_1, \cdots, \tau_q$ form a complete system of invariants of the group A. The number r is called the *rank of the group* A and the numbers $\tau_1, \cdots, \tau_q$ its *torsion coefficients.* We note that if all the elements of the group A are of prime order m, then its rank is equal to zero and all the torsion coefficients $\tau_1, \cdots, \tau_q$ are equal to m. In this case, the number q of torsion coefficients is called the rank modulo m of the group A, and it, together with m, forms a complete system of invariants of A.

C) If the coefficient group G is a cyclic group with generator g_1, the group L^r evidently admits of a finite system of generators

$$g_1A^r{}_1, \cdots, g_1A^r{}_{\alpha(r)},$$

where $A^r{}_1, \cdots, A^r{}_{\alpha(r)}$ is the set of all arbitrarily oriented r-simplexes of the complex K. By A), the subgroups Z^r and H^r of the group L^r, as well as the factor group $B^r = Z^r/H^r$, also admit of a finite system of generators.

Definition 15. Let $B^r{}_0$ be the r-dimensional Betti group of a complex K over the group of integers G_0. The rank of the group $B^r{}_0$ is called the r-dimensional *Betti number* of the complex K and is denoted by $p_0(r) = p(r)$. The torsion coefficients $\tau_1, \cdots, \tau_q$ of the group $B^r{}_0$ are called the r-dimensional *torsion coefficients* of the complex K, and are denoted by

$$\tau^r{}_1, \cdots, \tau^r{}_{q(r)}.$$

D) If the group G_m of residues modulo m, m a prime, is taken as the coefficient group, then every element of the group $L^r{}_m$, as well as every element of the subgroups $Z^r{}_m$ and $H^r{}_m$ of $L^r{}_m$ and the factor group

$$B^r{}_m = Z^r{}_m/H^r{}_m,$$

is also of order m.

Definition 16. Let $B^r{}_m$ be the r-dimensional Betti group of a complex K over the group G_m of residues modulo m, m a prime. The rank modulo m of the group $B^r{}_m$ is called the r-dimensional *Betti number* of the complex K modulo m and is denoted by $p_m(r)$.

Theorem 8. *The zero-dimensional Betti number $p_m(0)$ of an arbitrary complex K modulo m, $m = 0$ or a prime, is equal to the number p of components of the complex K. Moreover, the zero-dimensional Betti group $B^0{}_0$ of the complex K over G_0 does not have any torsion coefficients.*

Proof. By Theorem 7, the group $B^0{}_m$ is the direct sum of groups

$$C_1, \cdots, C_p,$$

each of which is isomorphic to the group G_m of residues modulo m. If $m = 0$, every group C_i is free, i.e., $B^0{}_0$ has no torsion coefficients, and its rank is p. If m is a prime, every group C_i is of order m, and the rank modulo m of the group $B^0{}_m$ is equal to p. This proves Theorem 8.

The Euler Characteristic. The Euler-Poincaré Formula

THEOREM 9. *If K is an n-complex, $\alpha(r)$ the number of r-simplexes of K, $p(r)$ the r-dimensional Betti number of K, and $p_m(r)$ the r-dimensional Betti number of K modulo m, m a prime, then we have*

$$\chi = \chi(K) = \sum_{r=0}^{n} (-1)^r \alpha(r) = \sum_{r=0}^{n} (-1)^r p(r) = \sum_{r=0}^{n} (-1)^r p_m(r).$$

The number χ is called the *Euler characteristic* of the complex K.

To prove Theorem 9, we reintroduce the notion of the rank of a group, and derive one of its properties.

E) If A_0 is an arbitrary commutative group, a system $x_1, \cdots, x_s$ of elements of A_0 will be called linearly independent if the relation

$$\lambda_1 x_1 + \cdots + \lambda_s x_s = 0,$$

where the λ_i are integers, implies $\lambda_1 = \cdots = \lambda_s = 0$. If the group A_0 admits of a finite maximal system of linearly independent elements

$$x_1, \cdots, x_\rho,$$

then A_0 will be said to be of finite rank ρ, denoted by $\rho_0(A_0)$. If the group A_0 has n linearly independent elements for every natural number n, then we set $\rho_0(A_0) = \infty$. It is easily proved that the rank of a group is one of its invariants, i.e., it is independent of the choice of a maximal system.

We shall show that if A_0 is a group with a finite number of generators, then definitions B) and E) yield the same number.

Denoting by x_i a generator of the cyclic group A_i and by y_j a generator of the cyclic group B_j (see B)), we show that $x_1, \cdots, x_r$ form a maximal linearly independent system. Suppose that

$$(1) \qquad \lambda_1 x_1 + \cdots + \lambda_r x_r = 0.$$

Since $A_0 = A_1 + \cdots + A_r + B_1 + \cdots + B_q$, (1) implies $\lambda_i x_i = 0$, and inasmuch as x_i is a free generator, $\lambda_i = 0$. Now, multiplication of an arbitrary element $x = \lambda_1 x_1 + \cdots + \lambda_r x_r + \mu_1 y_1 + \cdots + \mu_q y_q$ of the group

A_0 by $\lambda = \tau_q$ yields $\lambda x - \lambda\lambda_1 x_1 - \cdots - \lambda\lambda_r x_r = 0$, i.e., the system

$$x, x_1, \cdots, x_r$$

is linearly dependent.

F) If A_m is a group, all of whose elements are of prime order m, and G_m is the group of residues modulo m, then one can define an operation of multiplication of $\lambda \in G_m$ by $x \in A_m$. In fact, if β is any number of the residue class λ, then the product βx is obviously independent of the choice of β, and depends merely on the class λ itself. We may therefore set $\lambda x = \beta x$. A system $x_1, \cdots, x_s$ of elements of the group A_m is called linearly independent modulo m, if the relation $\lambda_1 x_1 + \cdots + \lambda_s x_s = 0$, where $\lambda_i \in G_m$, implies $\lambda_1 = \cdots = \lambda_s = 0$. If A_m has a maximal system $x_1, \cdots, x_\rho$ of linearly independent elements modulo m, we shall say that the rank modulo m of the group A_m is equal to ρ and denote it by $\rho_m(A_m)$. If, for every natural number n, there exists in A_m a system of n linearly independent elements modulo m, we set $\rho_m(A_m) = \infty$. It is easily proved that this definition of rank is a group invariant, i.e., is independent of the choice of a maximal system. We shall show that if A is a group with a finite system of generators, definitions B) and F) reduce to the same notion of rank modulo m.

Denote by y_j a generator of the cyclic group B_j (see B)), and assume that

$$\lambda_1 y_1 + \cdots + \lambda_q y_q = 0. \tag{2}$$

Since $A = B_1 + \cdots + B_q$, (2) implies $\lambda_j y_j = 0$; and since the order of the generator y_j is equal to m, $\lambda_j = 0$, $(\lambda_j \in G_m)$. Furthermore, if

$$y = \mu_1 y_1 + \cdots + \mu_q y_q$$

is any element of the group A, then the relation

$$y - \mu_1 y_1 - \cdots - \mu_q y_q = 0$$

shows that the system $y, y_1, \cdots, y_q$ is linearly dependent modulo m.

LEMMA. *Let m be zero or a prime, and A_m a group with the property that $mx = 0$ for every $x \in A_m$; i.e., if $m \neq 0$, every element of A_m is of order m, and if $m = 0$, A_m is arbitrary. If B_m is any subgroup of the group A_m, and $C_m = A_m/B_m$, then*

$$\rho_m(A_m) = \rho_m(B_m) + \rho_m(C_m). \tag{3}$$

Proof. To avoid having to distinguish the cases $m \neq 0$ and $m = 0$, call the ordinary linear independence (see E)) linear independence modulo 0.

If

(4) $$y_1, \cdots, y_s$$

and

(5) $$z_1, \cdots, z_t$$

are systems of elements, linearly independent modulo m, of the groups B_m and C_m, respectively, and $x_i \in A_m$ is in the coset z_i, then we shall show that the system

(6) $$x_1, \cdots, x_t, y_1, \cdots, y_s$$

is linearly independent modulo m in A_m.

Suppose that

(7) $$\lambda_1 x_1 + \cdots + \lambda_t x_t + \mu_1 y_1 + \cdots + \mu_s y_s = 0,$$

$$\lambda_j \in G_m, \mu_i \in G_m.$$

The corresponding relation for the factor group is $\lambda_1 z_1 + \cdots + \lambda_t z_t = 0$, and since the system (5) is independent, $\lambda_1 = \cdots = \lambda_t = 0$. Hence relation (7) reduces to $\mu_1 y_1 + \cdots + \mu_s y_s = 0$, whence, by (4),

$$\mu_1 = \cdots = \mu_s = 0.$$

Therefore the system (6) is independent.

The above implies that if either $\rho_m(B_m) = \infty$ or $\rho_m(C_m) = \infty$, then $\rho_m(A_m) = \infty$. Hence the lemma is proved for this case. We shall now show that if $\rho_m(B_m)$ and $\rho_m(C_m)$ are finite, and the systems (4) and (5) are maximal, then the system (6) is also maximal.

Suppose that $x \in A_m$ and let z be the coset of C_m which contains x. Since the system (5) is maximal,

(8) $$\nu z + \nu_1 z_1 + \cdots + \nu_t z_t = 0,$$

where $\nu \neq 0$, $\nu \in G_m$, $\nu_j \in G_m$. Relation (8) implies

(9) $$\nu x + \nu_1 x_1 + \cdots + \nu_t x_t = y \in B_m.$$

Since the system (4) is maximal, it follows that

(10) $$\mu y + \mu_1 y_1 + \cdots + \mu_s y_s = 0,$$

where $\mu \neq 0$, $\mu \in G_m$, $\mu_i \in G_m$. From (9) and (10) we obtain

(11) $$\mu\nu x + \mu\nu_1 x_1 + \cdots + \mu\nu_t x_t + \mu_1 y_1 + \cdots + \mu_s y_s = 0.$$

Here $\mu\nu \neq 0$, since, if $m = 0$, μ and ν are integers different from zero; and if $m \neq 0$, μ and ν are non-zero residues modulo m, m a prime, and their product is thus different from zero modulo m. Hence (11) establishes the linear dependence of the system $x, x_1, \cdots, x_t, y_1, \cdots, y_s$, which proves that the system (6) is maximal.

Proof of Theorem 9

Let m be zero or a prime, G_m the group of residues modulo m, and g a generator of the group G_m (G_0 is the group of integers). Further, let

$$A^r_1, \cdots, A^r_{\alpha(r)}$$

be the set of all arbitrarily oriented r-simplexes of the complex K. The elements $gA^r_1, \cdots, gA^r_{\alpha(r)}$ can be regarded as generators of the group L^r_m. It is easily established that this system is linearly independent modulo m. That it is maximal follows from the fact that it forms a system of generators. We have therefore

$$\rho_m(L^r_m) = \alpha(r). \tag{12}$$

In virtue of the lemma, we have

$$\rho_m(L^r_m) = \rho_m(Z^r_m) + \rho_m(L^r_m/Z^r_m), \qquad r = 0, 1, \cdots, n. \tag{13}$$

If $r > 0$, the groups L^r_m/Z^r_m and H_m^{r-1} are isomorphic (see §4, D)), and (13) reduces to

$$\rho_m(L^r_m) = \rho_m(Z^r_m) + \rho_m(H_m^{r-1}), \qquad r = 1, \cdots, n. \tag{14}$$

If $r = 0$, then $Z^0_m = L^0_m$, and hence

$$\rho_m(L^0_m) = \rho_m(Z^0_m). \tag{15}$$

Introducing the notation $\rho_m(H_m^{-1}) = 0$, the two relations (14) and (15) can be written as

$$\alpha(r) = \rho_m(Z^r_m) + \rho_m(H_m^{r-1}), \qquad \rho_m(H_m^{-1}) = 0, \qquad r = 0, 1, \cdots, n. \tag{16}$$

From the lemma and Defs. 15 and 16, it follows that

$$\begin{aligned} \rho_m(Z^r_m) &= \rho_m(H^r_m) + \rho_m(Z^r_m/H^r_m) = \rho_m(H^r_m) + \rho_m(B^r_m) \\ &= \rho_m(H^r_m) + p_m(r), \qquad r = 0, 1, \cdots, n. \end{aligned} \tag{17}$$

Since, by its very definition, $H^n_m = \{0\}$, relations (16) and (17) combined yield

$$\alpha(r) = p_m(r) + \rho_m(H_m^{r-1}) + \rho_m(H^r_m), \quad \rho_m(H_m^{-1}) = \rho_m(H^n_m) = 0, \qquad r = 0, 1, \cdots, n.$$

Multiplying the first of these by $(-1)^r$ and summing over r, we obtain

$$\textstyle\sum_{r=0}^n (-1)^r \alpha(r) = \sum_{r=0}^n (-1)^r p_m(r).$$

This proves Theorem 9.

Chapter II

THE INVARIANCE OF THE BETTI GROUPS

This chapter is devoted to the proof of the fact that, if the polyhedra $| K |$ and $| L |$ are homeomorphic, then the complexes K and L which generate them have isomorphic Betti groups in all dimensions. This enables one to speak of the Betti groups of the polyhedra themselves. The proof of this fact is not simple and requires the creation of a complicated technique, which is itself of great interest and is applicable not only to the proof of invariance, but also to the study of continuous mappings of one polyhedron into another.

The most interesting part of the machinery developed here is the construction of the so-called simplicial approximations. If φ is a continuous mapping of a polyhedron $| K |$ into a polyhedron $| L |$, the mapping φ is replaced by a so-called simplicial mapping, which can be completely treated from the combinatorial point of view, and which generates algebraic connections between the complexes K and L. It turns out, however, that, in order to make simplicial approximation possible, it is necessary to have the simplexes of the complex K sufficiently fine, and it is therefore necessary to subdivide the complex K. The complex K^* is called a subdivision of the complex K if $| K^* | = | K |$ and if every simplex of K^* is contained in some simplex of K. Just because of its generality, however, this general notion of subdivision is not easy to apply. We shall employ here instead the special so-called barycentric subdivisions. The relation between the complex K and its barycentric subdivision K', nevertheless, is so cumbersome as to make the proof of the isomorphism of the Betti groups of the complexes K and K' involved. This constitutes the most unpleasant part of the proof of the invariance of the Betti groups. The combination of the method of simplicial approximation with the operation of barycentric subdivision yields a proof of the invariance of the Betti groups.

§7. Simplicial mappings and approximations

In this section the notion of a simplicial mapping of a complex K into a complex L is defined, the behavior of chains, cycles, and homologies under a simplicial mapping of K into L is brought out, and it is proved that a continuous mapping φ of a polyhedron $| K |$ into a polyhedron $| L |$ can be approximated by a simplicial mapping, provided that certain restrictions are imposed on φ.

Simplicial Mapping

A) Let $A^r = (a_0, a_1, \cdots, a_r)$ be an r-simplex in R^m,

$$B^s = (b_0, b_1, \cdots, b_s)$$

an s-simplex in R^n, and f a mapping which assigns to each vertex a_i some vertex b_j (f need not be one-to-one). Assign to each point

$$x = \lambda^0 a_0 + \lambda^1 a_1 + \cdots + \lambda^r a_r \in A^r \tag{1}$$

the point $f(x) \in R^n$ by setting

$$f(x) = \lambda^0 f(a_0) + \lambda^1 f(a_1) + \cdots + \lambda^r f(a_r). \tag{2}$$

The resulting mapping obviously coincides with the initial one on the vertices a_i, and is a continuous mapping of the simplex A^r into the simplex B^s. It is called a *simplicial mapping* of A^r into B^s. The set $f(A^r)$ is a face D^k of the simplex B^s, where the simplex D^k spans those vertices b_j which are of the form $f(a_i)$. Moreover, if g is a simplicial mapping of B^s into the simplex $C^t = (c_0, c_1, \cdots, c_t)$, then gf is a simplicial mapping of A^r into C^t. Since f may map two or more distinct vertices of A^r into a single vertex of B^s, it is possible to combine the terms which contain the vertex b_j on the right-hand side of equation (2), with the result that (2) takes the form

$$f(x) = \mu^0 b_0 + \mu^1 b_1 + \cdots + \mu^s b_s, \tag{3}$$

where μ^j is the sum of all the λ^i for which $f(a_i) = b_j$. Since the λ^i satisfy (2) and (3) of Def. 4, the μ^j also satisfy these conditions, whence $f(x) \in B^s$. Relation (3) implies that $f(A^r)$ is equal to D^k, while the continuity of f on A^r follows from §2, B). The mapping gf, given by the formula

$$g[f(x)] = \lambda^0 g[f(a_0)] + \cdots + \lambda^r g[f(a_r)],$$

is simplicial in virtue of (2) and (3). Let us illustrate the above by a simple example.

Let $r = 3$, $s = 2$, and set

$$f(a_0) = f(a_2) = b_0, \qquad f(a_1) = f(a_3) = b_1.$$

Then $f(x) = (\lambda^0 + \lambda^2)b_0 + (\lambda^1 + \lambda^3)b_1$, $\mu^0 = \lambda^0 + \lambda^2$, $\mu^1 = \lambda^1 + \lambda^3$. Here $k = 1$ and $D^1 = (b_0, b_1)$.

DEFINITION 17. Let K and L be two complexes and f a continuous mapping of the polyhedron $|K|$ into the polyhedron $|L|$. If f is at the same time a simplicial mapping of the simplex A into some simplex B of L for every simplex A of K (see A)), then f is called a *simplicial mapping of the complex K into the complex L.*

The successive application of two simplicial mappings obviously again results in a simplicial mapping (see A)).

Def. 17 implies

1. If $a_0, a_1, \cdots, a_r$ are vertices of a simplex of the complex K, then $f(a_0), f(a_1), \cdots, f(a_r)$ are vertices of some simplex of the complex L.

It will be shown below (see B)) that if a mapping f, defined only on the vertices of the complex K, satisfies condition 1, then it can be extended, and moreover uniquely, to a simplicial mapping of all of K into L. This leads to the following definition.

Definition 18. A mapping f which assigns to every vertex of the complex K a vertex of the complex L in such a way as to satisfy condition 1, is called a *simplicial vertex mapping* of the complex K into the complex L. It may also be referred to as a *simplicial mapping of the abstract complex* $\mathfrak{K}$ *into the abstract complex* $\mathfrak{L}$, where $\mathfrak{K}$ and $\mathfrak{L}$ are the abstract complexes corresponding to the geometric complexes K and L.

If two or more distinct vertices of the simplex A are mapped by f into a single vertex, then the simplex A is said to be *degenerate under the mapping* f or simply *degenerate*.

B) If K and L are two geometric complexes and f a simplicial vertex mapping (see Def. 18) of the complex K into the complex L, then f can be extended to a mapping g of the whole polyhedron $|K|$ so that g is a simplicial mapping of the complex K into the complex L (see Def. 17). This extension, moreover, is unique.

Let $a_0, a_1, \cdots, a_k$ be the vertices of the complex K, $\mathfrak{K}$ the abstract complex corresponding to K, and N the natural realization of $\mathfrak{K}$ in the simplex $E^k = (e_0, e_1, \cdots, e_k)$ (see §2, F)). For simplicity we may allow a_i and e_i to correspond to the same vertex of the complex $\mathfrak{K}$. The relation

$$x = \lambda^0 a_0 + \lambda^1 a_1 + \cdots + \lambda^k a_k \tag{4}$$

assigns to each point $\lambda \in |N|$ a point $x \in |K|$. The resulting mapping $\lambda \rightarrow x$ of the polyhedron $|N|$ onto the polyhedron $|K|$ is one-to-one and bicontinuous (see §2, F)). The relation

$$g(x) = \lambda^0 f(a_0) + \lambda^1 f(a_1) + \cdots + \lambda^k f(a_k) \tag{5}$$

defines a continuous mapping $\lambda \rightarrow g(x)$ of the polyhedron $|N|$ into the polyhedron $|L|$. Hence relations (4) and (5) together define a continuous mapping g of $|K|$ into $|L|$. It is clear that $g(a_i) = f(a_i)$. Moreover, if $A^r = (a_{i_0}, a_{i_1}, \cdots, a_{i_r})$ is a simplex of K, then g defines a simplicial mapping of A^r into a simplex $B^s \in L$. We have thus found a simplicial mapping g of K into L which coincides with f on the vertices of K. The uniqueness of g is obvious, for if g coincides with f on all the vertices of some simplex A^r, it can be extended, by its very definition (see A)), to the whole simplex A^r in just one completely defined way (see (2)). This proves proposition B).

The Approximation Theorem

We shall now prove that continuous mappings can be approximated by simplicial mappings. To this end, we introduce an auxiliary notion, that of the *star of a complex*.

C) The set of all interior points of a simplex (see §2, A)) of a complex K will be referred to as an open simplex of K. It is easily seen that every point of the polyhedron $|K|$ is contained in exactly one open simplex of K. If a is a vertex of the complex K, the set-theoretic union of all the open simplexes of K with a as vertex is called the *star* of the vertex a in K and is denoted by $S(a)$, $S(a) \subset |K|$. Let us prove that every star $S(a)$ of K is an open set in $|K|$.

Let us set $F = |K| \backslash S(a)$ and show that $F = |K^*|$, where K^* is a subcomplex of K. This will prove our assertion, since every complex is compact and hence closed. Let K^* consist of all simplexes of K which do not have a as a vertex; then $|K^*| = F$. For, by construction, F is the set-theoretic union of all open simplexes of K not having a as vertex; but, if A is an open simplex which does not have a as vertex, then none of its faces have a as vertex, i.e., $\bar{A} \subset F$. Hence F is the set-theoretic union of all closed simplexes of K which do not have a as vertex, and $F = |K^*|$.

THEOREM 10. *Let φ be a continuous mapping of a complex K into a complex L which satisfies the star condition, i.e., with the property that for every star $S(a)$ of K there is at least one star $S(b)$ of L satisfying the condition $\varphi[S(a)] \subset S(b)$. Now assign to each vertex a of K a vertex $f(a)$ of L for which $\varphi[S(a)] \subset S[f(a)]$. Then f is a simplicial vertex mapping of K into L, and hence can be extended to a simplicial mapping of the whole complex K into the complex L. Under these conditions, f is called a simplicial approximation to φ, or φ is said to admit of a simplicial approximation f. Moreover, if $x \in |K|$, $D \in L$, and $\varphi(x) \in D$, then $f(x) \in D$.*

Proof. Let $x \in |K|$. Let A be that open simplex of K which contains x and B be that open simplex of L which contains $\varphi(x)$. Denoting the vertices of A by $a_0, a_1, \cdots, a_r$, we show that $f(a_i)$ is a vertex of B. Since $x \in A \subset S(a_i)$, we have

$$\varphi(x) \in \varphi[S(a_i)] \subset S[f(a_i)].$$

Moreover, since $\varphi(x) \in B$, the open simplex B is contained in the star $S[f(a_i)]$, and hence $f(a_i)$ is a vertex of B.

Since x is any point of $|K|$, A is an arbitrary open simplex of K, and this proves that f maps the vertices of a simplex of K into the vertices of a simplex of L, i.e., f is a simplicial mapping.

Since f is a simplicial mapping, it follows that $f(\bar{A}) = C \subset \bar{B}$, where C is a face of the simplex $\bar{B}$. Now, let D be a simplex of L which contains the point $\varphi(x)$ and T the complex consisting of D and all its proper faces. Since $\varphi(x)$ can lie in just one open simplex of L, namely B, it follows that $\bar{B} \in T$. Hence $\bar{B}$ is a face of D, which implies that C is also a face of D, and therefore

$$f(x) \in f(\bar{A}) = C \subset D.$$

This completes the proof of Theorem 10.

We remark that the simplicial approximation f to the continuous mapping φ defined in Theorem 10 is not unique, because there may be several stars $S(b)$ which satisfy the condition $\varphi[S(a)] \subset S(b)$. In the sequel we shall choose one of the possible approximations.

D) Let K, L, and M be three complexes, and φ, ψ continuous mappings of K into L and L into M, respectively. If f, g are simplicial approximations to φ and ψ, respectively, then gf is a simplicial approximation to $\psi\varphi$.

If a is a vertex of K, then $\varphi[S(a)] \subset S[f(a)]$, and therefore

$$\psi\{\varphi[S(a)]\} \subset \psi\{S[f(a)]\} \subset S\{g[f(a)]\},$$

which means that gf is a simplicial approximation to the mapping $\psi\varphi$.

Algebra of a Simplicial Mapping

What follows below is applicable to both abstract and geometric complexes, so that we shall not distinguish between them.

E) Let f be a simplicial mapping of a complex K into a complex L, and $A^r = \varepsilon(a_0, a_1, \cdots, a_r)$ an oriented simplex of K. If A^r is not degenerate under the mapping f, i.e., all the vertices of A^r are mapped into distinct vertices of L, $f(a_i) = b_i$, set

$$\hat{f}(A^r) = \varepsilon(b_0, b_1, \cdots, b_r) = B^r. \tag{6}$$

In the contrary case, set

$$\hat{f}(A^r) = 0. \tag{7}$$

Moreover, if $x = g_1 A^r{}_1 + \cdots + g_{\alpha(r)} A^r{}_{\alpha(r)}$ is any r-chain of K over G, the relation

$$\hat{f}(x) = g_1 \hat{f}(A^r{}_1) + \cdots + g_{\alpha(r)} \hat{f}(A^r{}_{\alpha(r)}) \tag{8}$$

associates with the chain x a chain $\hat{f}(x)$ of L of the same dimension and over the same group G. Hence we may say that the simplicial mapping f induces a *chain mapping* $\hat{f}$ given by (8). It is clear that

$$\hat{f}(x + y) = \hat{f}(x) + \hat{f}(y). \tag{9}$$

Moreover, $\hat{f}$ satisfies the following important condition:

$$(10) \qquad \Delta\hat{f}(x) = \hat{f}(\Delta x).$$

It suffices to prove (10) for $x = A^r$, the simplest integral chain.

If A^r is not degenerate, (6) implies

$$\Delta\hat{f}(A^r) = \sum_{i=0}^{r} \varepsilon(-1)^i(b_0, b_1, \cdots, b_{i-1}, b_{i+1}, \cdots, b_r).$$

Furthermore,

$$\Delta A^r = \sum_{i=0}^{r} \varepsilon(-1)^i(a_0, a_1, \cdots, a_{i-1}, a_{i+1}, \cdots, a_r).$$

Since A^r is not degenerate, none of its faces is degenerate, and the last relation yields

$$\hat{f}(\Delta A^r) = \sum_{i=0}^{r} \varepsilon(-1)^i(b_0, b_1, \cdots, b_{i-1}, b_{i+1}, \cdots, b_r).$$

Now, let A^r be degenerate, but so that $f(A^r)$ has dimension just one less than A^r, i.e., exactly two vertices of A^r correspond to a single vertex of its image. Since the order of the vertices is not essential, assume these to be a_0 and a_1, i.e., $f(a_0) = f(a_1) = b$, while all the remaining vertices

$$f(a_i) = b_i, \qquad i = 2, \cdots, r,$$

are distinct and different from b. By definition (see (7)), $\hat{f}(A^r) = 0$, and hence $\Delta\hat{f}(A^r) = 0$. Consequently, it suffices to prove that $\hat{f}(\Delta A^r) = 0$. To this end, consider

$$\Delta A^r = \sum_{i=0}^{r} \varepsilon(-1)^i(a_0, a_1, \cdots, a_{i-1}, a_{i+1}, \cdots, a_r).$$

There are just two simplexes, $(a_1, a_2, \cdots, a_r)$ and $(a_0, a_2, \cdots, a_r)$, on the right-hand side of the last equation, which are not degenerate; while the remaining simplexes are degenerate, since they each contain both vertices a_0 and a_1. Hence

$$\hat{f}(\Delta A^r) = \varepsilon(b, b_2, \cdots, b_r) - \varepsilon(b, b_2, \cdots, b_r) = 0.$$

If A^r is degenerate, and f lowers its dimension by more than one, then all its $(r-1)$-faces are degenerate, and relation (7) implies

$$\hat{f}(\Delta A^r) = 0 \quad \text{and} \quad \Delta\hat{f}(A^r) = 0.$$

This completes the proof of (10).

F) Let f be a simplicial mapping of a complex K into a complex L. If z is a cycle of K, then $\hat{f}(z)$ is a cycle of L; and if $z_1 \sim z_2$, then

$$\hat{f}(z_1) \sim \hat{f}(z_2).$$

In other words, $\hat{f}[Z^r(K)] \subset Z^r(L)$, and $\hat{f}[H^r(K)] \subset H^r(L)$.

In fact, by (10), $\Delta z = 0$ implies $\Delta\hat{f}(z) = \hat{f}(\Delta z) = 0$. If $z_1 - z_2 = \Delta x$, then (9) and (10) imply

$$\hat{f}(z_1) - \hat{f}(z_2) = \hat{f}(\Delta x) = \Delta\hat{f}(x).$$

This proves proposition F).

The above leads to the following basic definition.

DEFINITION 19. Let f be a simplicial mapping of a complex K into a complex L, and $B^r(K)$ and $B^r(L)$ the r-dimensional Betti groups of K and L over an arbitrary group G. If $z^* \in B^r(K)$ and z is any cycle of the homology class z^*, set

$$\tilde{f}(z^*) = \hat{f}(z)^*, \tag{11}$$

where $\hat{f}(z)^*$ is the homology class of $B^r(L)$ which contains the cycle $\hat{f}(z)$. It will be proved below that the mapping $\tilde{f}$ of $B^r(K)$ into $B^r(L)$ defined by (11) is unique, and moreover, that it is a homomorphism of $B^r(K)$ into $B^r(L)$. The mapping $\tilde{f}$ will be referred to as the *induced homomorphism of the simplicial mapping* f.

To show that $\tilde{f}$ is unique, let z_1 and z_2 be two cycles of z^*. Then $z_1 \sim z_2$, which implies $\hat{f}(z_1) \sim \hat{f}(z_2)$ (see F)), whence $\hat{f}(z_1)^* = \hat{f}(z_2)^*$. To prove that $\tilde{f}$ is a homomorphism, let u^*, v^* be two homology classes of $B^r(K)$, with $u^* + v^* = w^*$, and let u, v be cycles of u^*, v^*, respectively. Then

$$w = (u + v) \in w^*,$$

and

$$\tilde{f}(w^*) = \hat{f}(w)^* = \hat{f}(u + v)^* = [\hat{f}(u) + \hat{f}(v)]^*.$$

The last term of this equation is the homology class containing the sum $\hat{f}(u) + \hat{f}(v)$; but, in accordance with the definition of addition in a factor group, the class containing a sum is equal to the sum of the corresponding classes, i.e.,

$$[\hat{f}(u) + \hat{f}(v)]^* = \hat{f}(u)^* + \hat{f}(v)^* = \tilde{f}(u^*) + \tilde{f}(v^*).$$

Hence $\tilde{f}(w^*) = \tilde{f}(u^*) + \tilde{f}(v^*)$, and $\tilde{f}$ is a homomorphism.

G) If K, L, M are three complexes and f, g are simplicial mappings of K into L and L into M, respectively, then the induced mappings of the simplicial mapping $e = gf$ satisfy the relations

$$\hat{e} = \hat{g}\hat{f} \tag{12}$$

and

$$\tilde{e} = \tilde{g}\tilde{f}. \tag{13}$$

It suffices to prove (12) merely for an oriented simplex A^r of K. If A^r is not degenerate under e, then A^r is not degenerate under f and $f(A^r)$ is not

$x \in V$, i.e., $F^{r-1} \subset V$. This and the fact that $G^r \subset U$ imply $F^{r-1} = V$ and $G^r = U$, which proves proposition B).

Proposition C) gives an example of a cone construction which is needed in the sequel.

C) If $A^r = (a_0, a_1, \cdots, a_r)$ is a simplex of the Euclidean space R^n, then a point $\kappa \in R^n$ is in general position with respect to the set A^r if, and only if, the system $\kappa, a_0, a_1, \cdots, a_r$ is independent (see §1, A)), in which case $B^{r+1} = (\kappa, a_0, a_1, \cdots, a_r)$ is a simplex. If the points $\kappa, a_0, a_1, \cdots, a_r$ are independent, then $\kappa(A^r) = B^{r+1}$.

To prove C), assume that A^r contains two distinct points x_1 and x_2 such that the segments (κ, x_1) and (κ, x_2) intersect in a point y distinct from κ. If the barycentric coordinates of the points x_j, $j = 1, 2$, are denoted by $\lambda^0{}_j, \cdots, \lambda^r{}_j$, then

$$y = \alpha_j\kappa + \beta_j\lambda^0{}_j a_0 + \cdots + \beta_j\lambda^r{}_j a_r, \qquad \alpha_j \neq 1. \tag{5}$$

If relation (5) for $j = 1$ is subtracted from the same relation for $j = 2$, then

$$(\alpha_2 - \alpha_1)\kappa + (\beta_2\lambda^0{}_2 - \beta_1\lambda^0{}_1)a_0 + \cdots + (\beta_2\lambda^r{}_2 - \beta_1\lambda^r{}_1)a_r = 0. \tag{6}$$

Now, $\alpha_2 - \alpha_1 + \sum_{i=0}^r (\beta_2\lambda^i{}_2 - \beta_1\lambda^i{}_1) = 0$, and not all the coefficients of (6) vanish. In fact, if $\alpha_2 - \alpha_1 = 0$, then the vanishing of the remaining coefficients would imply that $x_1 = x_2$. Hence the points $\kappa, a_0, a_1, \cdots, a_r$ are linearly dependent.

Now, assume that if κ is in general position with respect to A^r, then the points $\kappa, a_0, a_1, \cdots, a_r$ are independent. We shall then show that the sets $\kappa(A^r)$ and B^{r+1} are identical. If $x \in A^r$, and the barycentric coordinates of x are $\lambda^0, \lambda^1, \cdots, \lambda^r$, then any $y \in \kappa(x)$ is of the form

$$y = \alpha\kappa + \beta\lambda^0 a_0 + \cdots + \beta\lambda^r a_r,$$

whence $y \in B^{r+1}$. Now, if

$$z = \mu\kappa + \mu^0 a_0 + \cdots + \mu^r a_r$$

is any point of B^{r+1}, assume that $\mu \neq 1$ (this will be true except in the obvious case $z = \kappa$), and set

$$\alpha = \mu, \qquad \beta = 1 - \mu, \qquad \lambda^i = \mu^i / \beta. \tag{7}$$

Then

$$z = \alpha\kappa + \beta\lambda^0 a_0 + \cdots + \beta\lambda^r a_r,$$

whence $z \in \kappa(A^r)$. Therefore $\kappa(A^r) = B^{r+1}$.

We shall now show that if κ is in general position with respect to A^r, then $\kappa, a_0, a_1, \cdots, a_r$ are independent. Assume that the points $\kappa, a_0,$

$a_1, \cdots, a_r$ are dependent (see §1, A)), i.e.,

$$(8) \qquad \nu\kappa + \nu^0 a_0 + \cdots + \nu^r a_r = 0, \qquad \nu + \nu^0 + \cdots + \nu^r = 0, \quad \nu \neq 0$$

Since this relation remains true if multiplied by an arbitrary number, its coefficients may be taken arbitrarily small. Moreover, if x_1 is any interior point of A^r with barycentric coordinates $\lambda^0_1, \cdots, \lambda^r_1$, set

$$(9) \qquad y = \alpha_1\kappa + \beta_1\lambda^0_1 a_0 + \cdots + \beta_1\lambda^r_1 a_r, \qquad \alpha_1 \neq 1, \beta_1 \neq 1.$$

Since all the coefficients in (9) are positive, addition of relations (8) and (9), the former taken with sufficiently small coefficients, yields the relation

$$y = (\alpha_1 + \nu)\kappa + (\beta_1\lambda^0_1 + \nu^0)a_0 + \cdots + (\beta_1\lambda^r_1 + \nu^r)a_r$$

with all coefficients positive. As in (7), setting

$$\alpha_2 = \alpha_1 + \nu, \qquad \beta_2 = 1 - \alpha_2, \qquad \lambda^i_2 = (\beta_1\lambda^i_1 + \nu^i)/\beta_2,$$

we get

$$y = \alpha_2\kappa + \beta_2\lambda^0_2 a_0 + \cdots + \beta_2\lambda^r_2 a_r.$$

Denoting by x_2 the point with barycentric coordinates $\lambda^0_2, \cdots, \lambda^r_2$, we show that $x_1 \neq x_2$. If $x_1 = x_2 = x$, then $y = \alpha_1\kappa + \beta_1 x$, $y = \alpha_2\kappa + \beta_2 x$, and since $\alpha_1 \neq \alpha_2 = \alpha_1 + \nu$, these are two distinct representations of $y \in (\kappa, x)$. This is impossible since (κ, x) is a 1-simplex, and α and β are barycentric coordinates with respect to it. This proves C).

D) Let K be a complex imbedded in the Euclidean space R^n and κ a point of R^n which is in general position with respect to the polyhedron $|K|$. Since κ is in general position with respect to $|K|$, it is in general position with respect to any simplex A of K, and hence $\kappa(A)$ is a simplex in R^n (see C)). Under these conditions, the set of all simplexes of the form $\kappa(A)$, $A \in K$, and their faces, forms a complex denoted by $\kappa(K)$; moreover, $|\kappa(K)| = \kappa(|K|)$. The faces which have to be added to the simplexes of the form $\kappa(A)$ to fill out $\kappa(K)$ are obviously the simplexes of K and the vertex (κ).

To prove that the simplexes of the set $\kappa(K)$ are properly situated, notice first that, if P and Q are two properly situated simplexes, then their respective boundaries consist of properly situated simplexes. Hence it suffices to show that any two simplexes of the form $\kappa(A)$ and $\kappa(B)$ $(A, B \in K)$ are properly situated. If A and B are disjoint, then the intersection of $\kappa(A)$ and $\kappa(B)$ contains just the point κ, their common vertex. If $A \cap B = C$, then C is the common face of A and B, and obviously $\kappa(A) \cap \kappa(B) = \kappa(C)$.

We shall now show that $|\kappa(K)| = \kappa(|K|)$. If $A \in K$, then $A \subset |K|$, and hence $\kappa(A) \subset \kappa(|K|)$, which means that $|\kappa(K)| \subset \kappa(|K|)$. If, on the other hand, $y \in \kappa(|K|)$, then there is a point $x \in |K|$ such that $y \in (\kappa, x)$;

and since there is a simplex A of K containing x, it follows that $y \in \kappa(A)$. Hence $\kappa(|K|) \subset |\kappa(K)|$, which completes the proof of proposition D).

Algebra of the Cone

E) Let K be a complex imbedded in the Euclidean space R^n and κ a point in general position with respect to the polyhedron $|K|$. If

$$A^r = \varepsilon\,(a_0, a_1, \cdots, a_r)$$

is an oriented simplex of K, denote by $\kappa(A^r)$ the oriented simplex

$$\varepsilon\,(\kappa, a_0, a_1, \cdots, a_r)$$

of the complex $\kappa(K)$ (see D)). If $x^r = g_1 A^r{}_1 + \cdots + g_k A^r{}_k$ is any r-chain of K, and we set

$$\kappa(x^r) = g_1\,\kappa(A^r{}_1) + \cdots + g_k\,\kappa(A^r{}_k), \tag{10}$$

then $\kappa(x^r)$ is an $(r + 1)$-chain of $\kappa(K)$ over the same coefficient group as x^r, whose boundary satisfies the relations

$$(11)\qquad \begin{aligned} \Delta\kappa(x^r) &= x^r - \kappa\Delta(x^r), \qquad r > 0, \\ \Delta\kappa(x^0) &= x^0 - I(x^0)(\kappa), \end{aligned}$$

where $I(x^0)$ is the Kronecker index of x^0 (see §5, D)).

The two relations (11) are immediately established for $x^r = A^r{}_i$, and are extended to an arbitrary chain x^r through multiplication by the coefficients g_i and summation over i.

The construction given here is applied to the proof of a simple proposition.

THEOREM 11. *Let A^r be an r-simplex, and denote by S^{r-1} the complex consisting of all the proper faces of A^r, by T^r the complex composed of A^r and all its proper faces. Then every s-cycle z^s, $s > 0$, of T^r is homologous to zero; while, in S^{r-1}, every s-cycle z^s, $0 < s < r - 1$, is homologous to zero, and every $(r - 1)$-cycle z^{r-1}, $r - 1 > 0$, is of the form $z^{r-1} = g\Delta(A^r)$, where g is an element of the coefficient group selected and A^r is the oriented simplex.*

Proof. With no restriction on generality, we can assume that the simplex $A^r = (a_0, a_1, \cdots, a_r)$ is imbedded in R^n and that there is a point κ such that the system $\kappa, a_0, a_1, \cdots, a_r$ is independent. Define a simplicial mapping f of the complex $\kappa(T^r)$ into the complex T^r by setting

$$f(\kappa) = a_0, f(a_i) = a_i, i = 0, 1, \cdots, r.$$

If z^s, $s > 0$, is any cycle of T^r, set $v = \kappa(z^s)$, so that $\Delta v = z^s$ (see (11)).

Then $z^s \sim 0$ in $\kappa(T^r)$, and, by construction, $\hat{f}(z^s) = z^s$. Since

$$z^s = \hat{f}(z^s) = \Delta\hat{f}(v) = \Delta u,$$

where u is a chain of T^r, it follows that $z^s \sim 0$ in T^r.

Now, if z^s is any cycle of S^{r-1}, then $z^s = \Delta(u)$, where u is a chain of T^r. If $s < r - 1$, the chain u is contained in S^{r-1}, because S^{r-1} contains every simplex of T^r of dimension less than r. Hence in this case $z^s \sim 0$ in S^{r-1}. If $s = r - 1$, since there is exactly one simplex A^r of dimension r in T^r, then denoting either one of the orientations of A^r again by A^r, we have $u = gA^r$, and hence $z^{r-1} = g\Delta(A^r)$. This proves Theorem 11.

Theorem 11 should be supplemented by the remark that zero-dimensional homologies in the complexes T^r and S^{r-1} are treated on the basis of §5. It need only be remarked that T^r is always connected, and S^{r-1} is connected unless $r - 1 = 0$, in which case S^{r-1} consists of two points.

§9. Barycentric subdivision of a complex

In this section we shall define the barycentric subdivision K' of a complex K by means of the cone construction (see §8, A)). The purpose of the operation of barycentric subdivision is to represent the polyhedron $|K|$, initially given by the complex K, in terms of the complex K', $|K'| = |K|$, whose simplexes are smaller than those of K. In this connection, it is important that the transition from K to K' be as simple as possible and allow the establishment of a relation between homologies in K and K'.

The geometric meaning of barycentric subdivision is very simple. We shall call the point of A^r, all of whose barycentric coordinates are equal to $1/(r + 1)$, the center of A^r. If K is of dimension zero, take $K = K'$. If K is of dimension one, to define K', divide each 1-simplex of K in half to obtain two 1-simplexes, thereby creating a new vertex, the center of the original 1-simplex. Now, assume that the operation of subdivision has already been defined for an n-complex. To determine K' for an $(n + 1)$-complex K, it is necessary to subdivide each $(n + 1)$-simplex A^{n+1} of K barycentrically, assuming that all simplexes of lesser dimension have already been subdivided. Assume that the boundary S^n of A^n has been barycentrically subdivided, and define the barycentric subdivision of A^{n+1} to be the cone $\kappa[(S^n)']$ whose vertex κ is the center of A^{n+1}.

Geometry of Barycentric Subdivision

Definition 20. Let us assign to every complex K, imbedded in the Euclidean space R^m, the complex K', likewise imbedded in R^m, and called the *barycentric subdivision* of K. If K is a 0-complex, put $K' = K$. Now, assume that the barycentric subdivision of an arbitrary n-complex has already been defined so as to satisfy the following conditions:

a) $$| K' | = | K |,$$

and b) if L is a subcomplex of K, then L' is a subcomplex of K'. To define the barycentric subdivision of an $(n + 1)$-complex K, denote by M the n-skeleton of K (see §5, A)) and by $A_1^{n+1}, A_2^{n+1}, \cdots, A_k^{n+1}$ the set of all $(n + 1)$-simplexes of K. Further, let S_i be the set of all proper faces of A_i^{n+1}, $S_i \subset M$, and let κ_i be the center of A_i^{n+1} (the point of A_i^{n+1} whose barycentric coordinates are all equal to $1/(n + 2)$). Since the complex S_i is of dimension n, its barycentric subdivision S'_i is defined, and $\kappa_i(S'_i)$ is a complex by §8, B). Now, define K' as the set of all simplexes contained in the complexes M' and $\kappa_i(S'_i)$, $i = 1, \cdots, k$. Then K' is a complex, and satisfies conditions a) and b).

Since K' is defined as the union of several complexes, it obviously satisfies condition 1 of Def. 5. To prove that K' satisfies condition 2 of Def. 5, let P and Q be two simplexes of K'. We shall show that they are properly situated by examining three possible cases.

Case 1. The simplexes P and Q are contained in M'. Since M' is a complex by the inductive hypothesis, P and Q are properly situated.

Case 2. $P \in M'$, $Q \in \kappa_i(S'_i)$. Since all simplexes of $\kappa_i(S'_i)$ are faces of simplexes of the form $\kappa_i(B)$, $B \in S'_i$, it suffices to consider the case $Q \in \kappa_i(B)$. Since $P \subset | M' | = | M |$ and $\kappa_i(B) \subset A_i^{n+1}$, it follows that

$$P \cap Q \subset | M | \cap A_i^{n+1} = | S_i | .$$

Again, $\kappa_i(B) \cap | S_i | = B$ implies that $P \cap Q \subset P \cap B$. Moreover, P and B, as two simplexes of M', are properly situated; whence, by §2, D), P and Q are also properly situated.

Case 3. $P \in \kappa_i(S'_i)$, $Q \in \kappa_j(S'_j)$. If $i = j$, P and Q are contained in the same complex and so are properly situated. If $i \neq j$, then, as in Case 2, assuming that $P = \kappa_i(A)$, $A \in S'_i$, $Q = \kappa_j(B)$, $B \in S'_j$, we have

$$P \subset A_i^{n+1}, \qquad Q \subset A_j^{n+1}, \qquad P \cap Q \subset A_i^{n+1} \cap A_j^{n+1}.$$

Since $i \neq j$, $A_i^{n+1} \cap A_j^{n+1} \subset | S_i | \cap | S_j |$, which implies that

$$P \cap Q \subset | S_i | \cap | S_j | ;$$

this in turn implies that $P \cap Q = P \cap | S_i | \cap Q \cap | S_j |$. Again,

$$P \cap | S_i | = \kappa_i(A) \cap | S_i | = A, \; Q \cap | S_j | = \kappa_j (B) \cap | S_j | = B,$$

whence $P \cap Q = A \cap B$. Since A and B are in M', they are properly situated, and hence P and Q are also properly situated (see §2, D)).

We shall now show that the barycentric subdivision K' of an $(n + 1)$-

complex K satisfies a) and b). We have

$$|K| = |M| \cup A_1^{n+1} \cup \cdots \cup A_k^{n+1}$$

and

$$|K'| = |M'| \cup |\kappa_1(S'_1)| \cup \cdots \cup |\kappa_k(S'_k)|.$$

By the inductive hypothesis, $|M| = |M'|$, and $A_i^{n+1} = |\kappa_i(S'_i)|$ by §8, B) and D); therefore $|K| = |K'|$.

Now, let L be any subcomplex of K, and N the n-skeleton of L. Number the $(n + 1)$-simplexes of K so that $A_1^{n+1}, \cdots, A_l^{n+1}$ is the set of all $(n + 1)$-simplexes of L. By definition, L' consists of all the simplexes in the complexes N' and $\kappa_j(S'_j)$, $j = 1, \cdots, l$. By the inductive hypothesis, N' is a subcomplex of M', because N is a subcomplex of M. Hence, since $l \leqq k$, L' is a subcomplex of K', and K' satisfies a) and b).

A) If K is any complex imbedded in the Euclidean space R^m, and

$$A_0, A_1, \cdots, A_r \tag{1}$$

is any decreasing sequence of simplexes of K, i.e., a sequence in which A_{i+1} is a proper face of A_i, $i = 0, 1, \cdots, r - 1$, then

$$(\sigma_0, \sigma_1, \cdots, \sigma_r) \tag{2}$$

is a simplex of K', where σ_i is the center of A_i. Conversely, every simplex P of K' can be given in this way. Hence the sequence (1) will be said to determine the simplex (2).

We shall prove A) by induction on the number of dimensions of K, retaining in this connection the notation of Def. 20.

If the simplex A_0 is of dimension less than $n + 1$, then all the simplexes of (1) are contained in M, and, by the inductive hypothesis, (2) is a simplex of $M' \subset K'$. If the dimension of A_0 is $n + 1$, then $A_0 = A_i^{n+1}$ and $\sigma_0 = \kappa_i$. If $r = 0$, $(\sigma_0) \in \kappa_i(S'_i) \subset K'$. If $r \neq 0$, the sequence $A_1, \cdots, A_r$ is contained in S_i; and, by the inductive hypothesis, $A = (\sigma_1, \cdots, \sigma_r)$ is a simplex of S'_i, whence

$$\kappa_i(A) = (\sigma_0, \sigma_1, \cdots, \sigma_r)$$

is a simplex of $\kappa_i(S'_i)$.

To prove the converse, let $P \in K'$. If $P \in M'$, then, by the inductive hypothesis, P is determined by (1). If $P \in \kappa_i(S'_i)$, the following cases may occur: a) $P \in S'_i$, and hence $P \subset M'$; b) $P = (\kappa_i)$, in which case P is determined by the sequence consisting of a single A_i^{n+1}; c) $P = \kappa_i(A)$, $A \subset S'_i$, in which case, by the inductive hypothesis, A is determined by some sequence $A_1, \cdots, A_r$ of faces of S_i, and P itself is determined by the sequence $A_i^{n+1}, A_1, \cdots, A_r$. This completes the proof of A).

The property of a barycentric subdivision stated in A) could have been used for its definition. Such a definition would perhaps be simpler, but, in my view, less intuitive. The proof of the facts that K' is a complex and that $|K'| = |K|$ would remain just as unwieldy.

We introduce now the notion of an iterated barycentric subdivision.

B) If K is an arbitrary complex, let $K^{(0)} = K$ and define $K^{(m)}$ as the barycentric subdivision of $K^{(m-1)}$. The complex $K^{(m)}$ will be called the barycentric subdivision of order m of K, or simply a *subdivision* of K. Whenever the order of the subdivision is immaterial, the subdivision of the complex K will be denoted by K with a Greek superscript, e.g., by K^{α}. Here, α does not indicate a number, so that the subdivisions $K^{\alpha}{}_1$ and $K^{\alpha}{}_2$ of two *distinct* complexes may be of different orders.

Let us estimate now the diameters of the simplexes of $K^{(m)}$ as compared with the diameters of the simplexes of K.

C) The diameter of a simplex A of R^n is equal to the maximum length of its 1-faces.

Let $A = (a_0, a_1, \cdots, a_r)$ be an r-simplex, and x, y two points of A, with the barycentric coordinates of x equal to $\lambda^0, \lambda^1, \cdots, \lambda^r$. The distance between x and y in R^n is given by the formula

$$\rho(x, y)^2 = (x - y)(x - y) = (x - y)^2.$$

If the vector x is given an increment h, then

$$\rho(x + h, y)^2 = (x - y)^2 + 2(x - y)\, h + h^2.$$

We shall show that if x is not a vertex of the simplex A, then there is a point $x + h$ of A for which

$$\rho(x + h, y) > \rho(x, y). \tag{3}$$

If x is not a vertex of A, at least two of its barycentric coordinates, say λ^0 and λ^1, are different from zero. Let ν be a positive number such that $\nu < \lambda^0/2$, $\nu < \lambda^1/2$, and set $h = \varepsilon\, \nu\, (a_0 - a_1)$, $\varepsilon = \pm 1$. It is clear that $x + h$ is contained in A. Now, choose that value for ε for which

$$(x - y)h \geqq 0;$$

then, for the chosen value of h, inequality (3) follows.

Hence, if x is not a vertex of A, the function $\rho(x, y)$ cannot attain its maximum. It does attain its maximum when x and y lie at the ends of the longest edge of A.

THEOREM 12. *Let K be an r-complex imbedded in R^n. If the diameter of every simplex of K does not exceed the number η, then the diameter of every simplex of $K^{(m)}$* (see B)) *does not exceed $[r/(r + 1)]^m\eta$. Consequently, the simplexes of $K^{(m)}$ can be made arbitrarily small by taking m sufficiently large.*

Proof. By C), the diameter of any simplex of K' does not exceed the greatest length of its 1-simplexes. Let (σ_0, σ_1) be any 1-simplex of K', where σ_0 is the center of a simplex $A_0 = (a_0, a_1, \cdots, a_s)$, and σ_1 is the center of a proper face $A_1 = (a_0, a_1, \cdots, a_t)$ of A_0 (see A)). Set $A = (a_{t+1}, \cdots, a_s)$ and let σ be the center of A. It is immediately verified that

$$\sigma_0 = [(t + 1)/(s + 1)]\sigma_1 + [(s - t)/(s + 1)]\sigma \qquad \text{(see §8, (2))}.$$

Thus the point σ_0 divides the segment (σ_1, σ) in the ratio $(s - t):(t + 1)$, and hence $\rho(\sigma_0, \sigma_1) = [(s - t)/(s + 1)]\rho(\sigma_1, \sigma)$. However, since σ_1 and σ are contained in A_0, $\rho(\sigma_1, \sigma)$ does not exceed the diameter of A_0, whence $\rho(\sigma_0, \sigma_1) \leqq [(s - t)/(s + 1)]\eta$. Since $0 \leqq s \leqq r$ and $0 \leqq t \leqq s - 1$, the diameter of an arbitrary 1-simplex of K' does not exceed $[r/(r + 1)]\eta$; which, by C), implies that the diameter of any simplex of arbitrary dimension of K' does not exceed $[r/(r + 1)]\eta$.

The proof given above immediately implies the assertion of the theorem for a barycentric subdivision $K^{(m)}$ of order m of K. This proves Theorem 12.

Algebra of Barycentric Subdivision

Our problem now is to indicate the transition from each chain x of K to some definite chain x' of K' when we pass from K to its barycentric subdivision K'.

D) Let K be a complex of arbitrary dimension, and K' the barycentric subdivision of K. We shall assign to each r-chain x of K over G an r-chain x' of K' over the same coefficient group G. The chain x' is called the barycentric subdivision of the chain x, and is defined as follows. If x is a 0-chain, set $x' = x$. Assuming that the barycentric subdivision of the n-chains of K has already been defined, we shall define the barycentric subdivision of the simplest $(n + 1)$-chain of K, $x = A$, where A is an oriented $(n + 1)$-simplex of K. Let S be the set of all proper faces of A and κ the center of A, so that $\kappa(S') \subset K'$. By the inductive hypothesis, the barycentric subdivision $(\Delta A)'$ of the boundary ΔA of A has already been defined, since $(\Delta A)'$ is a chain of S'. Set $A' = \kappa[(\Delta A)']$ (see §8, E)), and if

$$x = g_1 A_1 + \cdots + g_k A_k$$

is any $(n + 1)$-chain of K, put $x' = g_1 A'_1 + \cdots + g_k A'_k$. Then any chain x of K satisfies the following important relation:

$$\Delta(x') = (\Delta x)'. \tag{4}$$

If $K^{(m)}$ is the barycentric subdivision of order m of K, define the chain $x^{(m)}$ inductively by letting $x^{(0)} = x$ and $x^{(m+1)} = (x^{(m)})'$. If $K^{(m)}$ is denoted by K^α (see B)), then $x^{(m)}$ will be denoted by x^α. Relation (4) immediately implies

$$\Delta(x^\alpha) = (\Delta x)^\alpha. \tag{5}$$

Relation (4) will be proved by induction. It is obvious for a 0-chain. We shall prove it for an oriented $(n + 1)$-simplex A on the assumption that it is true for an arbitrary n-chain. Since

$$\Delta A' = \Delta\kappa[(\Delta A)'] = (\Delta A)' - \kappa[\Delta(\Delta A)'], \tag{6}$$

and ΔA is n-dimensional, it follows by the inductive hypothesis that $\Delta(\Delta A)' = (\Delta\Delta A)' = 0$. Hence relation (6) reduces to (4).

E) If z is a cycle of K, then z^α is a cycle of K^α. If the cycles z_1 and z_2 are homologous in K, then the cycles $z^\alpha{}_1$ and $z^\alpha{}_2$ are homologous in K^α. This proposition follows immediately from (5).

§10. A lemma on the covering of a simplex, and its application

The present section is a digression from the basic theme of this book, homology theory, but closely borders on it. None of the exposition which follows it is based on the contents of this section.

A proof of Sperner's lemma and two applications of this lemma are given here. The applications are: 1) A proof of the fact that an r-simplex has dimension r in the sense of Def. 8, and 2) A proof of the fact that a continuous mapping of a simplex into itself always has a fixed point, i.e., a point which is mapped into itself.

The question as to whether or not the number of dimensions of a simplex is a topological invariant was one of the difficult problems of mathematics. It was solved in the affirmative by Brouwer and Lebesgue at the beginning of this century. Sperner's lemma is the result of a long process of perfecting the proof of the invariance of the dimension number of a simplex.

Sperner's Lemma

A) Let K be a complex, K^α a subdivision of K (see §9, B)), and let a be any vertex of K^α. Denote by $C(a)$ the simplex of smallest dimension of K which contains a, and assign to the vertex $a \in K^\alpha$ one of the vertices $f(a) \in K$ of the simplex $C(a)$. Then the mapping f of the vertices of K^α into the vertices of K is simplicial (see Def. 18), and every chain x of K satisfies the relation

$$\hat{f}(x^\alpha) = x. \tag{1}$$

Let us prove A). Def. 20 of the barycentric subdivision K' of a complex K implies that each simplex of K' is contained in at least one simplex of K. This statement is obviously valid also for an arbitrary subdivision K^α of K. Now, let B be a simplex of K^α and denote by $C(B)$ the simplex of least dimension of K which contains B. The simplex $C(B)$ is obviously uniquely determined, since the intersection of any two simplexes of K is again a simplex of K, unless this intersection is empty. If b is any vertex of B, then clearly $C(b)$ is a face of $C(B)$ which may coincide with $C(B)$. Hence $f(b)$ is a vertex of $C(B)$, and f maps all the vertices of B into vertices of $C(B)$, i.e., f is a simplicial vertex mapping.

Relation (1) will be proved by induction on the number of dimensions of the chain x. It is obvious for a 0-chain. We shall prove it for the simplest r-chain, an oriented r-simplex A, on the assumption that it is true for any $(r - 1)$-chain of K. Every simplex B of the chain A^α with non-vanishing coefficient is obviously contained in the simplex A, and hence $C(B)$ is a face of A. Therefore $f(B)$ is a face of A. Now, regarding B as an oriented simplex, $\hat{f}(B)$ is zero if B is degenerate under the mapping f, and $+A$ or $-A$ otherwise. Hence

$$\hat{f}(A^\alpha) = kA, \tag{2}$$

and it need only be shown that $k = +1$. To this end, take the boundary of both sides of equation (2), obtaining

$$\Delta\hat{f}(A^\alpha) = \hat{f}(\Delta A^\alpha) = \hat{f}[(\Delta A)^\alpha] = k\Delta A.$$

Setting $\Delta A = x$, we get $\hat{f}(x^\alpha) = kx$ from the last equality; and since x is an $(r - 1)$-chain, it satisfies (1), whence $k = 1$.

To extend the above from A to an arbitrary r-chain x, it suffices to remark that both sides of (1) are linear in x. This proves A).

LEMMA. *Let* $A = (a_0, a_1, \cdots, a_r)$ *be an* r*-simplex and* $\Sigma = \{F_0, F_1, \cdots, F_r\}$ *a closed covering of* A (see §3, B)), *with the property that an arbitrary face* $C = (a_{i_0}, a_{i_1}, \cdots, a_{i_s})$ *of* A *is wholly contained in the union of the sets of the system* $\Sigma' = \{F_{i_j}, j = 0, 1, \cdots, s\}$. *Then there exists a point* a *which is contained in every set of the system* Σ, *i.e., the covering* Σ *is of order* $r + 1$.

Proof. Assume that there is no point a which is contained in every set of the system Σ. Then the order of Σ does not exceed r, and there exists a positive δ for which the system Σ_δ composed of the sets

$$H(F_i, \delta), i = 0, 1, \cdots, r,$$

is again of order less than or equal to r (see §3, C)).

Denote by T the complex consisting of all the faces of A, $|T| = A$, and by T^α a subdivision of T so fine that the diameter of every simplex of T^α is less than δ (see Theorem 12). If b is any vertex of T^α and

$$C(b) = (a_{i_0}, a_{i_1}, \cdots, a_{i_s}),$$

then, by hypothesis, the face $C(b) = C$ of the simplex A is contained in the union of the sets of the corresponding system Σ'. Hence there is a set F_{i_q} of Σ' which contains b. A correspondence, of the sort indicated in A), between each vertex $b \in T^\alpha$ and a vertex $f(b) \in T$ is established by setting $f(b) = a_{i_q}$; and moreover, $f(b) = a_i$ implies that $b \in F_i$. We now show that if $B = (b_0, b_1, \cdots, b_r)$ is any r-simplex of T^α, then B is degenerate under the mapping f, i.e., it cannot be mapped onto the whole simplex A. Otherwise, all the vertices $f(b_i)$, $i = 0, 1, \cdots, r$, would be distinct, which would mean that $b_i \in F_{j_i}$, $i = 0, 1, \cdots, r$, where all the indices $j_0, j_1, \cdots, j_r$ are distinct. Hence the simplex B would intersect every set of Σ. However, if B intersects F_i, then $B \subset H(F_i, \delta)$ since the diameter of B is less than δ. Hence B is contained in every set of Σ_δ, which is impossible, whence every r-simplex of T^α is degenerate under the mapping f.

Now, if A is an oriented simplex, then A^α is an integral r-chain of T^α; and since every r-simplex B of T^α is degenerate under f, it follows that $\hat{f}(A^\alpha) = 0$. This contradicts (1) and proves the lemma.

B) In order that a covering Σ satisfy the conditions of the lemma, it is sufficient that each set F_i not intersect the face

$$A_i = (a_0, a_1, \cdots, a_{i-1}, a_{i+1}, \cdots, a_r)$$

opposite the vertex a_i.

Indeed, if i is not one of the numbers $i_0, i_1, \cdots, i_s$, then C is a face of the simplex A_i (see the lemma), and by hypothesis this face does not intersect F_i. Hence C can intersect only sets of Σ'. Since Σ is a covering of A, the face C is contained in the union of the sets of Σ, and therefore C is contained in the union of the sets of Σ'. Consequently, Σ satisfies the hypothesis of the lemma.

Dimension of a Polyhedron

It will be shown here that if K is an r-complex (see Def. 5), then the dimension of the polyhedron $|K|$ is equal to r (see Def. 8). Hence the dimension of a complex is a topological invariant of the complex, since Def. 8 is topologically invariant. In particular, this also answers the question as to the invariance of the dimension number of a simplex. The nontrivial part of the proof consists in showing that the dimension of an r-simplex is not less than r; this is carried through by means of Sperner's lemma. The trivial part of the proof is the construction of an ε-mapping of the polyhedron $|K|$ of order $r + 1$.

C) Let K be any r-complex, K' the barycentric subdivision of K, and c a vertex of K (c is obviously also a vertex of K'). The set of all simplexes of K' with vertex c, and all their faces, is called a *barycentric star* of K with center c, and is denoted by $B(c)$. If the diameter of all simplexes of K' is less than $\varepsilon/2$, then obviously the diameter of the polyhedron $|B(c)|$ is less than ε. If $c_0, c_1, \cdots, c_k$ is the set of vertices of K, then the polyhedra $|B(c_i)|$, $i = 0, 1, \cdots, k$, form a closed covering Σ of order $r + 1$ of the polyhedron $|K|$.

If B is a simplex of K', it is determined by a decreasing sequence $A_0, A_1, \cdots, A_{p-1}$ of simplexes of K (see §9, A)). If A_{p-1} is a 0-simplex, i.e., if $A_{p-1} = (c_i)$, then B is in the barycentric star $B(c_i)$. If the dimension of A_{p-1} is positive, denoting by c_i one of the vertices of this simplex and setting $A_p = (c_i)$, the sequence

$$A_0, A_1, \cdots, A_{p-1}, A_p \tag{3}$$

determines a simplex D of the complex $B(c_i)$, where B is a face of D. Hence, in this case again, the simplex B is contained in the barycentric star $B(c_i)$. Consequently, every simplex of K' is contained in at least one barycentric star, which means that the system Σ is a covering of $|K|$.

If σ is a vertex of the complex $B(c_i)$ and A is the simplex of K whose center is σ (see §8, B)), we shall show that c_i is a vertex of the simplex A. Since σ is a vertex of the complex $B(c_i)$, there is a simplex D in $B(c_i)$ with σ and c_i among its vertices. Let us assume that the simplex D is determined by the sequence (3); then the simplex A appears in this sequence. Since

$$A_p = (c_i)$$

is a face of every simplex of the sequence (3), it follows that c_i is a vertex of A.

Suppose that the sets of a subsystem of Σ have a non-empty intersection P. Since every set of Σ is a polyhedron corresponding to a subcomplex of K', P is likewise a polyhedron corresponding to a subcomplex of K', and hence contains a vertex σ of K'. If A is the simplex of K whose center is σ, then the centers of all the complexes $B(c_i)$ which contain σ are vertices of the simplex A. Since the dimension of A is not greater than r, it follows that the number of such complexes $B(c_i)$ does not exceed $r + 1$. Hence the order of Σ does not exceed $r + 1$.

If A is an r-simplex of K with vertices $a_0, a_1, \cdots, a_r$, then the vertex σ, the center of the simplex A, is contained in every complex

$$B(a_i), \ i = 0, 1, \cdots, r.$$

Therefore the order of Σ is not less than $r + 1$. This completes the proof of C).

THEOREM 13. *If K is an r-complex, $|K|$ has dimension r in the sense of Def.* 8.

Proof. Let ε be an arbitrary positive number and let K^α be a subdivision of the complex K such that the diameters of all simplexes of K^α do not exceed $\varepsilon/2$. Application of proposition C) to the complex K^α yields a closed

ε-covering of $|K|$ of order $r + 1$. Hence the dimension of $|K|$ does not exceed r.

To prove that the dimension of $|K|$ is not less than r, it suffices to show that this is the case for an arbitrary r-simplex A of K, since, by Def. 8, the dimension of a subspace cannot be greater than the dimension of the space.

Let $A = (a_0, a_1, \cdots, a_r)$ be an r-simplex of K and let

$$A_i = (a_0, a_1, \cdots, a_{i-1}, a_{i+1}, \cdots, a_r)$$

be the face of the simplex A opposite the vertex a_i. It is clear that no point of A can be common to all the faces A_i. Indeed, the face A_i is defined by the equation $\lambda^i = 0$ (see §2, C)), and the set of all such equations implies the relation $\lambda^0 = \lambda^1 = \cdots = \lambda^r = 0$, which cannot be satisfied by the barycentric coordinates of a point. Hence there exists a positive number ε such that the intersection of all the sets of the system Σ^*_ε consisting of the sets $H(A_i, \varepsilon)$, $i = 0, 1, \cdots, r$, is empty (see §3, C)). We shall show that every closed ε-covering $\Sigma = \{C_0, C_1, \cdots, C_k\}$ of the simplex A is of order greater than or equal to $r + 1$.

The set C_j of the system Σ cannot intersect all the faces A_i, for otherwise C_j would be contained in every set of the system Σ^*_ε, which is impossible. Hence we may assign to each index j, $j = 0, 1, \cdots, k$, an index $g(j)$, $0 \leqq g(j) \leqq r$, such that C_j does not intersect $A_{g(j)}$. If F_i is the union of all those sets C_j of the system Σ for which $g(j) = i$, then F_i does not intersect A_i, $i = 0, 1, \cdots, r$. Hence the system $F_0, F_1, \cdots, F_r$ satisfies the condition of proposition B), and, in accordance with the lemma, there is a point a common to all the sets $F_0, F_1, \cdots, F_r$. Since $a \in F_i$, and F_i is the union of certain sets of Σ, there exists an index j_i such that $a \in C_{j_i}$ and $g(j_i) = i$. The indices of the sets C_{j_i}, $i = 0, 1, \cdots, r$, are all distinct, because each index j was assigned a unique integer $g(j)$. It follows that a is contained in $r + 1$ distinct elements of the covering Σ, and hence the order of this covering is not less than $r + 1$. This proves Theorem 13.

Brouwer's Theorem

The theorem concerning the existence of a fixed point of a continuous mapping of a simplex into itself will be obtained here as a very simple application of Sperner's lemma.

THEOREM 14. *If $A = (a_0, a_1, \cdots, a_r)$ is an r-simplex and φ is a continuous mapping of A into itself, then there exists a point $a \in A$ for which $\varphi(a) = a$. The point a is called a fixed point of the mapping φ.*

Proof. Denote by $\lambda^i(p)$, $\mu^i(p)$, $i = 0, 1, \cdots, r$, the barycentric coordinates of a point $p \in A$ and its image $\varphi(p)$, respectively. If F_i is the set of all points p of the simplex A for which

$$\lambda^i(p) \geqq \mu^i(p), \tag{4}$$

we shall show that the system $\Sigma = \{F_0, F_1, \cdots, F_r\}$ satisfies the conditions of the lemma.

The continuity of φ immediately implies that every set of the system Σ is closed.

Let $C = (a_{i_0}, a_{i_1}, \cdots, a_{i_s})$ be any face of the simplex A (not excluding A itself). Let $p \in C$ and assume that p is not contained in any set of the system $\Sigma' = \{F_{i_j}, j = 0, 1, \cdots, s\}$. Then, by (4),

$$\lambda^{i_j}(p) < \mu^{i_j}(p), \qquad j = 0, 1, \cdots, s.$$

Adding all these inequalities, we get

$$\sum_{j=0}^{s} \lambda^{i_j}(p) < \sum_{j=0}^{s} \mu^{i_j}(p).$$

Since the point p is contained in the simplex C, the left side of this inequality is equal to one, while the right side cannot exceed one. Hence the inequality is impossible.

Consequently, in accordance with the lemma, there exists a point $a \in A$ which is contained in every set of Σ, whence

$$(5) \qquad \lambda^0(a) \geqq \mu^0(a), \quad \lambda^1(a) \geqq \mu^1(a), \cdots, \quad \lambda^r(a) \geqq \mu^r(a).$$

If the system (5) were to contain at least one strict inequality, say $\lambda^i(a) > \mu^i(a)$, then addition of all the inequalities (5) would yield

$$\lambda^0(a) + \lambda^1(a) + \cdots + \lambda^r(a) > \mu^0(a) + \mu^1(a) + \cdots + \mu^r(a).$$

This is a contradiction, since each side is equal to one. Hence it follows that

$$\lambda^0(a) = \mu^0(a), \lambda^1(a) = \mu^1(a), \cdots, \lambda^r(a) = \mu^r(a),$$

i.e., $a = \varphi(a)$. This proves Theorem 14.

§11. The invariance of the Betti groups under barycentric subdivision

In this section we shall derive a relation between homologies in a complex K and a subdivision K^α of K (see §9, B)). In particular, the Betti groups of K and K^α will be shown to be isomorphic.

THEOREM 15. *Let K be any complex, and leg K^α be a subdivision of K* (see §9, B)). *If $\mathfrak{z}$ is any r-dimensional homology class of K and z is a cycle of $\mathfrak{z}$, then denote by $\mathfrak{z}^\alpha$ the homology class of K^α which contains the cycle z^α. Under these conditions the single-valued mapping $\mathfrak{z} \to \mathfrak{z}^\alpha$* (see §9, E)) *is an isomorphism of the r-dimensional Betti group $B^r(K)$ of K onto the r-dimensional Betti group $B^r(K^\alpha)$ of K^α.*

In the sequel we shall sometimes identify the homology classes $\mathfrak{z}$ and $\mathfrak{z}^\alpha$ and treat the groups $B^r(K)$ and $B^r(K^\alpha)$ as identical.

The proof of Theorem 15 is preceded by a lemma.

LEMMA. *If K is a complex, K^α a subdivision of K, and x a chain of K^α*

whose boundary Δx is of the form $\Delta x = z^\alpha$, where z is a cycle of K, then there exists a chain y of K with boundary $\Delta y = z$ such that $x - y^\alpha$ is a cycle homologous to zero in K^α.

We shall show first that Theorem 15 follows from the lemma.

A) Theorem 15 follows from the lemma. Retaining the notation of Theorem 15, set $\mathfrak{z}^\alpha = \varphi(\mathfrak{z})$. The mapping φ assigns to each element of the group $B^r(K)$ an element of the group $B^r(K^\alpha)$, and is clearly a homomorphism of $B^r(K)$ into $B^r(K^\alpha)$. It suffices to show that this homomorphism is an isomorphism onto all of $B^r(K^\alpha)$.

We shall show first that φ is an isomorphism. If $\mathfrak{z}^\alpha = 0$, then $z^\alpha \sim 0$ in K^α, i.e., there is a chain x of K^α with $\Delta x = z^\alpha$. Application of the lemma to the chain x yields a chain y of K with $\Delta y = z$, i.e., $z \sim 0$ in K or $\mathfrak{z} = 0$. Hence $\varphi(\mathfrak{z}) = 0$ implies $\mathfrak{z} = 0$, and φ is therefore an isomorphism.

To show that φ is a mapping onto the whole group $B^r(K^\alpha)$, let $\mathfrak{r}$ be any element of $B^r(K^\alpha)$ and x an element of the homology class $\mathfrak{r}$. Since x is a cycle of K^α, $\Delta x = 0^\alpha$, where 0 is the trivial cycle of K. Hence the lemma, with $z = 0$, is applicable. Thus there is a chain y of K such that $\Delta y = 0$ and $x - y^\alpha \sim 0$ in K^α. It is clear that $\varphi(\mathfrak{y}) = \mathfrak{r}$, where $\mathfrak{y}$ is the homology class of K which contains y. Hence φ maps $B^r(K)$ onto all of $B^r(K^\alpha)$. This proves proposition A).

Proof of the Lemma

We shall prove the lemma only for $K^\alpha = K'$, i.e., for the first barycentric subdivision of K. The proof can be extended to any subdivision $K^{(m)}$ by an obvious induction of m. For $K^\alpha = K'$, the lemma is proved by induction on the number of dimensions of the complex K. If K is a 0-complex, the lemma is obvious. Suppose that it is true for every n-complex; then, in virtue of A), Theorem 15 also holds for every n-complex.

Let K be an $(n + 1)$-complex, M its n-skeleton, and $A_1^{n+1}, \cdots, A_k^{n+1}$ the set of all arbitrarily oriented $(n + 1)$-simplexes of K. Denote by S_i the set of all proper faces of A_i^{n+1}, by κ_i the center of A_i^{n+1}, and set $T_i = \kappa_i(S'_i)$. By the inductive hypothesis, both the lemma and Theorem 15 hold for S_i, since S_i has dimension n. Hence the homology properties of the complex S'_i are the same as those of the complex S_i, whose homology properties have already been examined in Theorem 11. Starting with the homology properties of S'_i and the relation $T_i = \kappa_i(S'_i)$, we now turn to the homology properties of T_i.

Leb x_i be an r-chain of T_i of the form $\kappa_i(z_i)$, where z_i is a chain of S'_i, with the property that its boundary Δx_i is contained in S'_i. Then: a) if $r \leqq n$, there exists a chain y_i in S'_i such that $x_i - y_i$ is a cycle homologous to zero in T_i, and b) if $r = n + 1$, $x_i = g_i(A_i^{n+1})'$, where g_i is an element of the coefficient group over which the chains are taken.

If $r = 1$, $\Delta x_i = \Delta\kappa_i(z_i) = z_i - I(z_i)\kappa_i$ (see §8, (11)), and since Δx_i is contained in S'_i, it follows that $I(z_i)\kappa_i = 0$, or $I(z_i) = 0$, i.e., in this case z_i is a 0-cycle of S'_i with Kronecker index equal to zero. If $r > 1$ (see §8, (11)), $\Delta x_i = \Delta\kappa_i(z_i) = z_i - \kappa_i(\Delta z_i)$, which implies that $\kappa_i(\Delta z_i) = 0$, or $\Delta z_i = 0$, i.e., z_i is an $(r - 1)$-cycle of S'_i.

a) If $r \leqq n$, the dimension of z_i does not exceed $n - 1$. By Theorem 15, the cycle z_i is homologous to zero in S'_i if $r > 1$, because every cycle of dimension less than n but greater than zero is homologous to zero in S_i (see Theorem 11). If $r = 1$, then, by the above, $I(z_i) = 0$. Since $n \geqq r = 1$, S_i is connected and therefore $z_i \sim 0$ in this case also (see §5, E)). Hence there is a chain y_i in S'_i such that $\Delta y_i = z_i$, and setting $v_i = \kappa_i(y_i)$, we have

$$\Delta v_i = y_i - \kappa_i(\Delta y_i) = y_i - x_i, \quad \text{i.e.,} \quad x_i - y_i \sim 0 \quad \text{in} \quad T_i.$$

b) If $r = n + 1$, then z_i has dimension n. If $n = 0$, the Kronecker index of z_i is zero, and hence, as is easily seen, z_i is of the form $z_i = g_i\Delta A'_i$. This proves the assertion for $n = 0$, since $\Delta A'_i = (\Delta A_i)'$. Now let n be greater than zero. By Theorem 15, there is a cycle u_i in S_i such that $z_i \sim u'_i$ in S'_i; but, since z_i has the same dimension as S'_i, the homology reduces to an equality, and $z_i = u'_i$. By Theorem 11, the cycle u_i of S_i is of the form $g_i\Delta A_i^{n+1}$. Hence $z_i = g_i(\Delta A_i^{n+1})'$, i.e., $x_i = g_i\kappa_i[(\Delta A_i^{n+1})'] = g_i(A_i^{n+1})'$. This completes the proof of a) and b).

We assumed in the preceding that $x_i = \kappa_i(z_i)$, and hence that the dimension of x_i was not less than one. We shall now show that:

c) If x_i is a 0-chain of T_i, there exists a 0-chain y_i of S'_i such that $x_i - y_i \sim 0$ in T_i.

If a is a vertex of S'_i, then $+(\kappa_i, a)$ is a simplex of T_i with boundary $+(a) - (\kappa_i)$, i.e., $+(\kappa_i) \sim +(a)$ in T_i. Replacing the simplex $+(\kappa_i)$ by $+(a)$ in x_i, we obtain the required chain y_i.

Now, let x be a chain of K' satisfying the conditions of the lemma. Since the dimension of $\Delta x = z'$ is not greater than n, z is a chain of M, and hence z' is a chain of M'. Denote by x_i the sum of all the members of the linear form x which contain simplexes with vertex κ_i; then x_i is a chain of T_i, and we shall show that Δx_i is a chain of S'_i. In fact, the chain $x - x_i$ does not contain any simplexes with vertex κ_i, and hence the boundary $\Delta x - \Delta x_i$ likewise does not contain such simplexes. The chain Δx is contained in M' and also does not contain any simplexes with vertex κ_i. Hence the difference $\Delta x_i = \Delta x - (\Delta x - \Delta x_i)$ of these two chains contains no simplex with vertex κ_i. Thus, the chain Δx_i is contained in S'_i and a), b), and c) are applicable to it.

Now let us consider two cases.

First case: The dimension of the chain x is less than $n + 1$. By a) and c), there is a chain y_i of S'_i such that $x_i - y_i \sim 0$ in T_i. Setting

$$x^* = x - (x_1 - y_1) - \cdots - (x_k - y_k),$$

we obtain $\Delta x^* = \Delta x = z'$ and therefore $x^* - x \sim 0$ in K'. The chain x^* obviously does not contain a simplex with vertex κ_i, $i = 1, 2, \cdots, k$, and hence x^* is contained in M'. Therefore the lemma is applicable to x^*, i.e., there exists a chain y of M such that $\Delta y = z$ and $x^* - y' \sim 0$ in M'. Hence $x - y' \sim 0$ in K'. This proves the first case.

Second case: The dimension of the chain x is $n + 1$. By b), the chain x_i is of the form $x_i = g_i(A_i^{n+1})'$. If

$$y = g_1 A_1^{n+1} + \cdots + g_k A_k^{n+1},$$

the chain $x - y'$ obviously does not contain any simplex with vertex κ_i, $i = 1, 2, \cdots, k$. Since $x - y'$ is an $(n + 1)$-chain, it is equal to zero, and hence $x = y'$. The boundary of $x - y'$ is $(z - \Delta y)' = 0$. Therefore $\Delta y = z$, since the barycentric subdivision of a chain is zero only if the chain itself is zero. This proves the second case and completes the proof of the lemma, which by A) proves Theorem 15.

§12. The invariance of the Betti groups

We come finally to a proof of the invariance of the Betti groups based on the technique presented in the preceding sections of this chapter.

THEOREM 16. *If K_1 and K_2 are complexes such that the polyhedra $|K_1|$ and $|K_2|$ are homeomorphic, then the Betti groups $B^r(K_1, G)$ and $B^r(K_2, G)$ are isomorphic for any coefficient group G.*

This theorem is a direct consequence of the more precise Theorem 18. The latter establishes an explicit isomorphism between the groups $B^r(K_1, G)$ and $B^r(K_2, G)$ when a definite homeomorphism φ of the polyhedron $|K_1|$ onto the polyhedron $|K_2|$ is given. The formulation and proof of Theorem 18 are preceded by several preliminary remarks.

Preliminary Remarks and a Lemma

A) Let K and L be two complexes, K^α and L^β subdivisions of K and L, respectively, and f a simplicial mapping of K^α into L^β. The mapping f induces a homomorphism $\tilde{f}$ of the group $B^r(K^\alpha, G)$ into the group $B^r(L^\beta, G)$ (see Def. 19). On the other hand, Theorem 15 establishes a definite isomorphism between $B^r(K^\alpha, G)$ and $B^r(K, G)$, as well as between $B^r(L^\beta, G)$ and $B^r(L, G)$. Hence $\tilde{f}$ can be regarded as a homomorphism of $B^r(K, G)$ into $B^r(L, G)$. More precisely, the homomorphism $\tilde{f}$ of $B^r(K, G)$ into $B^r(L, G)$ is described as follows: let $\mathfrak{x}$ be any element of the group $B^r(K, G)$, x a cycle of the class $\mathfrak{x}$, and x^α the subdivision of x in K^α. Then $\hat{f}(x^\alpha)$ is a cycle of L^β (see §7, F)), and by Theorem 15, there exists a cycle y of L

whose subdivision y^β is homologous to $\hat{f}(x^\alpha)$ in L^β. If $\mathfrak{n}$ is the homology class which contains y, then $\tilde{f}(\mathfrak{r}) = \mathfrak{n}$.

B) If K and L are two complexes and φ is a continuous mapping of the polyhedron $|K|$ into the polyhedron $|L|$, then there exists an integer $m \geqq 0$ for which the mapping φ of the complex $K^{(m)}$ into L satisfies the star condition (see Theorem 10).

There exists a positive number ε such that every subset F of the polyhedron $|L|$ of diameter less than ε is wholly contained in one of the stars $S(b)$ of the complex L. In fact, let us assume the contrary i.e., that for every natural number t there exists a set F_t of $|L|$ of diameter less than $1/t$ which is not wholly contained in any one of the stars of the complex L. Since $|L|$ is compact and the diameters of the sets F_t tend to zero, there exists a point c in $|L|$, and arbitrary neighborhood of which contains an infinite number of the sets F_t. Taking as a neighborhood of c the star $S(b)$ of K which contains c, at least one of the sets F_t is contained wholly in $S(b)$, and we arrive at a contradiction. This proves the existence of the required ε.

Since $|K|$ is compact, φ is uniformly continuous, and therefore there is a positive number δ such that

$$\rho[\varphi(x), \varphi(y)] < \varepsilon \tag{1}$$

for $x, y \in |K|$ and $\rho(x, y) < \delta$.

If η is the greatest of the diameters of the simplexes of K, choose an m large enough so that $[n/(n+1)]^m\eta < \delta/2$; then the diameter of every star $S(a)$ of $K^{(m)}$ is less than δ (see Theorem 12). By (1), the diameter of $\varphi[S(a)]$ is less than ε, and hence $\varphi[S(a)]$ is contained in at least one of the stars $S(b)$. Thus the mapping φ of $K^{(m)}$ into L satisfies the star condition. This proves B).

C) If K' is the barycentric subdivision of an arbitrary complex K, then every star of K' is contained in some star of K.

Let σ be any vertex of K' and A the simplex of K whose center is σ. If $B = (\sigma_0, \sigma_1, \cdots, \sigma_r)$ is any simplex of the star $S(\sigma)$ of K', then $\sigma = \sigma_i$. The open simplex B is obviously contained in the open simplex A_0 (see §9, A)), and since $A_i = A$ is a face of A_0, the star $S(\sigma)$ is contained in the union $S(A)$ of all open simplexes with A as face. If a is a vertex of A, it is clear that the star $S(a)$ of K contains $S(A)$, and hence $S(\sigma) \subset S(a)$. This proves C).

LEMMA. *Let f be a simplicial mapping of a complex K into a complex L and let K^α be a subdivision of K* (see §9, B)). *If $K^\alpha \neq K$, then f is not a simplicial mapping of K^α into L, but it does satisfy the star condition, and hence there exists* (see Theorem 10) *a simplicial mapping f^α of K^α into L which approximates f. In addition, if x is a chain of K,*

$$\hat{f}^\alpha(x^\alpha) = \hat{f}(x). \tag{2}$$

In particular, if $L = K$ and f is the identity mapping of K onto itself, then $\hat{f}^\alpha(x^\alpha) = x$.

Proof. We shall show first that f satisfies the star condition.

Let a be a vertex of K. If $f(a) = b$ and A is any open simplex of K with vertex a, it is easily seen that $f(A)$ is an open simplex of L with vertex b (see §7, A)). Hence $f[S(a)] \subset S(b)$, and this, by C), implies that the mapping f of K^α into L also satisfies the star condition.

Relation (2) will be proved by induction on the number of dimensions of the chain x. It is obvious for a 0-chain. We shall prove that it is true for an oriented r-simplex A of K on the assumption that it is true for any $(r - 1)$-chain.

Let T be the set of all faces of the simplex A. Then $f(\mid T \mid) = D$, where D is a simplex of L. All vertices of the comples T^α are mapped by f into points of D, and hence f^α maps every simplex of T^α either into D or a face of D (see Theorem 10). Consider the following two cases:

a) If the dimension of D is less than r, then all r-simplexes of T^α are degenerate under f^α, and hence $\hat{f}^\alpha(A^\alpha) = 0$, which implies that $\hat{f}(A) = 0$.

b) If the dimension of D is r, then $\hat{f}(A)$ is the simplex D oriented in some fashion. On the other hand, since every r-simplex of T^α is either degenerate under f^α or maps onto D, it follows that

$$\hat{f}^\alpha(A^\alpha) = k\hat{f}(A), \tag{3}$$

where k is an integer. To show that $k = 1$, apply the operation Δ to (3) obtaining

$$\Delta\hat{f}^\alpha(A^\alpha) = \hat{f}^\alpha(\Delta A^\alpha) = \hat{f}^\alpha[(\Delta A)^\alpha] = k\Delta\hat{f}(A) = k\hat{f}(\Delta A).$$

If ΔA is denoted by x, the last relation implies that

$$\hat{f}^\alpha(x^\alpha) = k\hat{f}(x).$$

Since, by the inductive hypothesis, relation (2) holds for an $(r - 1)$-chain x, it follows that $k = 1$. Hence $\hat{f}^\alpha({A^\alpha}_i) = \hat{f}(A_i)$ for an arbitrary oriented simplex A_i of K. Multiplication of the last relation by the coefficient g_i and summation over i yields (2) for an arbitrary r-chain. This proves the lemma.

We note an important consequence of the lemma just proved.

D) Let f be a simplicial mapping of a complex K into a complex L, K^α a subdivision of K, and f^α a simplicial mapping of K^α into L which approximates f. The mapping f^α induces a homomorphism $\hat{f}^\alpha$ of $B^r(K^\alpha)$ into $B^r(L)$, which, by A), can also be interpreted as a homomorphism of $B^r(K)$ into $B^r(L)$. On the other hand, f also induces the homomorphism $\hat{f}$ of $B^r(K)$ into $B^r(L)$, and it turns out that the homomorphisms $\hat{f}$ and $\hat{f}^\alpha$ of $B^r(K)$ into $B^r(L)$ are identical. In particular, if $L = K$ and f is the identity mapping of K onto itself, then the homomorphism $\tilde{f}^{\alpha}$ is the identity mapping of $B^r(K)$ onto itself.

If $x^* \in B^r(K)$ and x is a cycle of the homology class x^*, then $\hat{f}^{\alpha}(x^{\alpha})$ is a cycle of L and the homology class $\hat{f}^{\alpha}(x^{\alpha})^*$ containing it is, according to A), $\tilde{f}^{\alpha}(x^*)$. On the other hand, $\hat{f}(x)$ is also a cycle of L and the homology class $\hat{f}(x)^*$ containing it is $\tilde{f}(x^*)$. By the lemma, $\hat{f}^{\alpha}(x^{\alpha}) = \hat{f}(x)$, whence $\tilde{f}^{\alpha}(x^*) = \tilde{f}(x^*)$. This proves D).

The above lemma also yields a simple proof of the invariance of the dimension of a polyhedron.

THEOREM 17. *If* $|K_1|$ *and* $|K_2|$ *are homeomorphic polyhedra, their corresponding complexes* K_1 *and* K_2 *have equal dimensions.* This enables us to speak of the dimension of a polyhedron.

Proof. Assume that the dimension n of the complex K_1 is greater than the dimension of the complex K_2, and let φ be a homeomorphism of K_2 onto K_1. Choose subdivisions $K^{\alpha}{}_2$ and $K^{\alpha}{}_1$ of K_2 and K_1, respectively, sufficiently fine to insure the existence of simplicial mappings f of $K^{\alpha}{}_2$ into K_1 and g of $K^{\alpha}{}_1$ into $K^{\alpha}{}_2$ which approximate φ and φ^{-1}, respectively. Then the simplicial mapping fg of $K^{\alpha}{}_1$ into K_1 approximates the identity mapping $\varphi\varphi^{-1}$, and hence, by the lemma,

$$\hat{f}[\hat{g}(x^{\alpha})] = x \tag{4}$$

holds for every chain x of K_1.

On the other hand, every n-simplex of $K^{\alpha}{}_1$ is degenerate under the mapping g because $K^{\alpha}{}_2$ contains no simplexes of dimension n. Hence $\hat{g}(x^{\alpha}) = 0$ for every n-chain x of K, whence $\hat{f}[\hat{g}(x^{\alpha})] = 0$. However, this contradicts relation (4), because K_1 contains a non-trivial n-chain x. This proves Theorem 17.

The Fundamental Theorem

THEOREM 18. *Let* φ_1 *be a homeomorphism of a complex* K_1 *into a complex* K_2, $\varphi_1^{-1} = \varphi_2$, *and* $K^{\alpha}{}_1$, $K^{\alpha}{}_2$ *subdivisions of the given complexes for which the mapping* φ_1 *of* $K^{\alpha}{}_1$ *into* $K^{\alpha}{}_2$ *satisfies the star condition. If the mapping* $f^{\alpha}{}_1$ *of* $K^{\alpha}{}_1$ *into* $K^{\alpha}{}_2$ *is a simplicial approximation to* φ_1, *then*

a) *the homomorphism* $\tilde{f}^{\alpha}{}_1$ *of the group* $B^r(K_1)$ *into the group* $B^r(K_2)$ *is independent of the choice of* $K^{\alpha}{}_1$, $K^{\alpha}{}_2$, *and* $f^{\alpha}{}_1$, *and hence can be denoted by* $\tilde{\varphi}_1$,

$$\tilde{\varphi}_1[B^r(K_1)] \subset B^r(K_2);$$

b) *the homomorphism* $\tilde{\varphi}_1$ *is an isomorphism of* $B^r(K_1)$ *onto* $B^r(K_2)$; *and*

c) *if the isomorphism* $\tilde{\varphi}_2$ *of* $B^r(K_2)$ *onto* $B^r(K_1)$ *is induced by* φ_2 *in the same manner, then the isomorphisms* $\tilde{\varphi}_1$ *and* $\tilde{\varphi}_2$ *are inverse to each other.*

Proof. In order to prove a) and b), let us introduce, in addition to K^{α}_1 and K^{α}_2, two other subdivisions K^{β}_1 and K^{β}_2 of the given complexes for which the mapping φ_1 of K^{β}_1 onto K^{β}_2 satisfies the star condition, and denote by the mapping f^{β}_1 of K^{β}_1 into K^{β}_2 a simplicial approximation to φ_1.

Since K^{α}_1 and K^{β}_1 are barycentric subdivisions of the same complex K_1, one of the subdivisions is finer than the other, say K^{β}_1 is finer than K^{α}_1. Choose a subdivision K^{γ}_2 of K_2 so fine that the mapping φ_2 of K^{γ}_2 onto K^{β}_1 satisfies the star condition. Denote by f^{α}_2 and f^{β}_2 simplicial approximations to φ_2 of K^{γ}_2 into K^{α}_1 and K^{γ}_2 into K^{β}_1, respectively. In addition, let K^{γ}_1 be a subdivision of K_1 such that the mapping φ_1 of K^{γ}_1 into K^{γ}_2 satisfies the star condition, and denote by f^{γ}_1 a simplicial approximation to φ_1 of K^{γ}_1 into K^{γ}_2.

The resulting system of mappings can be represented schematically as follows:

$$K^{\alpha}_2 \underset{f^{\alpha}_1}{\overset{\varphi_1}{\longleftarrow}} K^{\alpha}_1 \underset{f^{\alpha}_2}{\overset{\varphi_2}{\longleftarrow}} K^{\gamma}_2 \underset{f^{\gamma}_1}{\overset{\varphi_1}{\longleftarrow}} K^{\gamma}_1 .$$

In the diagram the arrows refer to the mappings, with the given homeomorphisms written above the arrows and their simplicial approximations below the arrows. Substitution of the index β for the index α yields the alternative mapping scheme which will not be written down.

The simplicial mappings induce homomorphisms of the corresponding Betti groups which can likewise be schematically represented as:

$$B^r(K^{\alpha}_2) \underset{\bar{f}^{\alpha}_1}{\longleftarrow} B^r(K^{\alpha}_1) \underset{\bar{f}^{\alpha}_2}{\longleftarrow} B^r(K^{\gamma}_2) \underset{\bar{f}^{\gamma}_1}{\longleftarrow} B^r(K^{\gamma}_1),$$

$$B^r(K_2) \leftarrow B^r(K_1) \leftarrow B^r(K_2) \leftarrow B^r(K_1).$$

In this scheme the Betti groups of the subdivided complexes are written on the first line, while the groups of the original complexes, for which there are also induced homomorphisms (see A)), are shown on the second line. Again, substitution of β for α yields the alternative scheme.

The mapping $f^{\alpha}_1 f^{\alpha}_2$ of K^{γ}_2 into K^{α}_2 is a simplicial approximation to $\varphi_1\varphi_2$ (see §7, D)), and hence the homomorphism $\bar{f}^{\alpha}_1 \bar{f}^{\alpha}_2$ of $B^r(K_2)$ onto itself is the identity homomorphism (see the lemma). The kernel of the homomorphism $\bar{f}^{\alpha}_1 \bar{f}^{\alpha}_2$ contains the kernel of $\bar{f}^{\alpha}_2$, and since $\bar{f}^{\alpha}_1 \bar{f}^{\alpha}_2$ is the identity homomorphism, its kernel is zero. Therefore:

(5) *The kernel of the homomorphism* $\bar{f}^{\alpha}_2$ *is zero.*

Since $\bar{f}^{\alpha}_1 \bar{f}^{\alpha}_2$ maps $B^r(K_2)$ identically onto itself, we have

$$B^r(K_2) = \bar{f}^{\alpha}_1\bar{f}^{\alpha}_2 B^r(K_2) \subset \bar{f}^{\alpha}_1 B^r(K_1),$$

and hence

(6) $$\bar{f}^{\alpha}{}_1 B^r(K_1) = B^r(K_2).$$

The mapping $f^{\alpha}{}_2 f^{\gamma}{}_1$ of $K^{\gamma}{}_1$ into $K^{\alpha}{}_1$ is a simplicial approximation to the identity mapping $\varphi_2\varphi_1$, and in the same way we obtain

(7) *The kernel of the homomorphism $\bar{f}^{\gamma}{}_1$ is zero,*

(8) $$\bar{f}^{\alpha}{}_2 B^r(K_2) = B^r(K_1).$$

It follows from (5) and (8) that $\bar{f}^{\alpha}{}_2$ is an isomorphism of $B^r(K_2)$ onto $B^r(K_1)$, and since $\bar{f}^{\alpha}{}_1 \bar{f}^{\alpha}{}_2$ is the identity mapping, $\bar{f}^{\alpha}{}_1$ and $\bar{f}^{\alpha}{}_2$ are inverse isomorphisms:

(9) $$\bar{f}^{\alpha}{}_1 = (\bar{f}^{\alpha}{}_2)^{-1}.$$

Similarly, we conclude that $\bar{f}^{\alpha}{}_2$ and $\bar{f}^{\gamma}{}_1$ are inverse isomorphisms:

(10) $$\bar{f}^{\gamma}{}_1 = (\bar{f}^{\alpha}{}_2)^{-1}.$$

It is seen from (9) and (10) that $\bar{f}^{\alpha}{}_1$ and $\bar{f}^{\gamma}{}_1$ are identical:

(11) $$\bar{f}^{\alpha}{}_1 = \bar{f}^{\gamma}{}_1.$$

Replacing α by β, we get

(12) $$\bar{f}^{\beta}{}_1 = \bar{f}^{\gamma}{}_1.$$

From (11) and (12) it follows that $\bar{f}^{\alpha}{}_1 = \bar{f}^{\beta}{}_1$, which proves a). It has already been proved that $\bar{f}^{\alpha}{}_1$ is an isomorphism, whence b) also holds.

We can now apply proposition a), which has just been proved, to the mapping φ_2 of K_2 onto K_1. If the induced homomorphism of $B^r(K_2)$ onto $B^r(K_1)$ is denoted by $\bar{\varphi}_2$, relation (9) shows that the isomorphisms $\bar{\varphi}_1$ and $\bar{\varphi}_2$ are inverse to each other. This proves c), and completes the proof of Theorem 18.

The Betti Groups of a Polyhedron

Let us extend somewhat the notion of a polyhedron.

DEFINITION 21. A metric space P is called a *polyhedron* if it is homeomorphic to a polyhedron $|K|$ in the previous sense of the term (see Def. 6). If σ is a homeomorphism of the complex K onto the space P, the pair (σ, K) will be called a *triangulation* of the polyhedron P. The r-dimensional Betti group of K will be referred to as the r-dimensional *Betti group* of this triangulation and will be denoted by $B^r(\sigma, K)$.

Theorem 16 enables us to speak of the Betti groups of a polyhedron P, because the Betti groups of any two triangulations of the polyhedron P are isomorphic. However, on the basis of Theorem 16, the Betti group of a polyhedron P is determined only to within an isomorphism, so that its elements do not retain their individuality. Theorem 18 leads to the following more concrete definition.

DEFINITION 22. If P is a polyhedron and (σ_1, K_1), (σ_2, K_2) are two triangulations of P, then $\sigma_2^{-1}\sigma_1 = \varphi$ is a topological mapping of K_1 onto K_2, whence, by Theorem 18, φ induces an isomorphism $\tilde{\varphi}$ of the group $B^r(\sigma_1, K_1)$ onto the group $B^r(\sigma_2, K_2)$. The elements $x_1 \in B^r(\sigma_1, K_1)$ and $x_2 \in B^r(\sigma_2, K_2)$ will be regarded as equivalent, $x_1 \sim x_2$, if $x_2 = \tilde{\varphi}(x_1)$. This relation is obviously reflexive, its symmetry follows from Theorem 18, while its transitivity will be proved below. The set of all equivalent elements of the r-dimensional Betti groups of all the triangulations of a polyhedron P will be considered an element of the r-dimensional Betti group $B^r(P)$ of P. If $\xi \in B^r(P)$, $x \in \xi$, and $x \in B^r(\sigma, K)$, then x will be called a *representative* of the element ξ in the triangulation (σ, K). If ξ and η are two elements of $B^r(P)$, and x and y are their representatives in the triangulation (σ, K), then the sum $\xi + \eta$ is defined as that element of $B^r(P)$ which contains $x + y$. By Theorem 18, since $\tilde{\varphi}$ is an isomorphism, it follows that this sum is independent of the triangulation (σ, K).

To show that the above equivalence relation is transitive, let (σ_i, K_i), $i = 1, 2, 3$, be any three triangulations of the polyhedron P. In addition, let $\sigma_2^{-1}\sigma_1 = \varphi$, $\sigma_3^{-1}\sigma_2 = \omega$, and let $x_i \in B^r(\sigma_i, K_i)$, $i = 1, 2, 3$, be three elements such that $x_1 \sim x_2$ and $x_2 \sim x_3$. Then

$$x_2 = \tilde{\varphi}(x_1), \qquad x_3 = \tilde{\omega}(x_2),$$

i.e.,

$$x_3 = \tilde{\omega}[\tilde{\varphi}(x_1)].$$

We shall show that the isomorphism $\tilde{\omega}\tilde{\varphi}$ corresponds to the mapping $\sigma_3^{-1}\sigma_1$. Let K^α_3 be any subdivision of K_3, and denote by K^α_2 and K^α_1 subdivisions of K_2 and K_1, respectively, sufficiently fine to insure the existence of simplicial approximations g of K^α_2 into K^α_3 and f of K^α_1 into K^α_2 to the mappings $\sigma_3^{-1}\sigma_2$ and $\sigma_2^{-1}\sigma_1$, respectively. Then Theorem 18 implies that

$$\tilde{\omega} = \tilde{g}, \qquad \tilde{\varphi} = \tilde{f}, \text{ i.e., } \tilde{\omega}\tilde{\varphi} = \tilde{g}\tilde{f}.$$

Since gf is a simplicial approximation to the continuous mapping

$$\sigma_3^{-1}\sigma_2\sigma_2^{-1}\sigma_1 = \sigma_3^{-1}\sigma_1 = \omega\varphi$$

(see §7, D)), the isomorphism $\tilde{\omega}\tilde{\varphi}$ corresponds to the topological mapping $\sigma_3^{-1}\sigma_1$. This proves transitivity.

Chapter III

CONTINUOUS MAPPINGS AND FIXED POINTS

If P and Q are two geometric figures, e.g., two polyhedra, then all the continuous mappings of P into Q can be divided into equivalence classes. Two such mappings are regarded as equivalent if one of them can be transformed into the other by means of a continuous deformation (see Def. 23). The classification of continuous mappings from this point of view is one of the basic problems of modern topology. This problem is as yet in the initial stage of solution. Homology theory makes it possible to construct some invariants of the mapping classes. If φ is a continuous mapping of a polyhedron $|K|$ into a polyhedron $|L|$, then φ induces homomorphisms $\tilde{\varphi}$ of the Betti groups of the complex K into the Betti groups of the complex L (see Theorem 20). These homomorphisms are invariants not only of the mapping φ itself, but of the mapping class which contains φ, as well. It is natural to refer to these as homology invariants. As a matter of fact, only in very special cases do the homology invariants form a complete system. Nevertheless, these invariants are very important, and the first sections of this chapter will be concerned with their construction.

If the polyhedra P and Q are identical, one can speak of fixed points of continuous mappings φ of the polyhedron P into itself. A point x of P is called a fixed point of the mapping φ if $\varphi(x) = x$.

Many existence theorems of analysis reduce to the question of the existence of fixed points of a mapping, and hence the problem of fixed points of a mapping occupies an important position in topology. Great advances have been made in its solution, which, in a certain sense, may be considered complete. Every isolated fixed point of a mapping is described by its index, an integer which is positive, negative, or zero. It has been proved that the sum of the indices of all fixed points of a given mapping φ of a polyhedron P into itself can be expressed in terms of homology invariants of φ. Hence this sum does not depend on φ itself, but is determined by the mapping class which contains φ. Therefore the problem concerning the sum of the indices of the fixed points must be regarded as solved, but this is not a solution of the problem in its full scope. It can happen, for example, that the sum of the indices of a mapping is equal to zero. In that case, it is impossible, on the basis of this result, to infer the existence of fixed points. And yet the given mapping, and all those equivalent to it, may have fixed points, even though the sum of the indices is zero. In this case also the result gives no information about the number of distinct fixed points of the mapping. Again, it may occur that the sum of the indices is very large, while the mapping has only one fixed point of large index. Nevertheless, the result expressing the sum of the indices in terms of homology invariants is a very important one and is one of the most significant in combinatorial topology. We shall, however, confine ourselves here to proving that a mapping has at least one fixed point if the homology invariant expressing the sum of the indices does not vanish.

§13. Homotopic mappings

In this section we shall give a precise definition of the homotopy of mappings and indicate an important method for the study of this notion. This method is based on the concept of a topological product and a continuous mapping of this product.

Definition 23. Let P and Q be two metric spaces, and for each real number t, $0 \leqq t \leqq 1$, let φ_t be a continuous mapping of the space P into the space Q. The family of mappings φ_t will be called *continuous* if the function $\varphi_t(x)$, $x \in P$, is a continuous function of the two variables, the number t and the point x. More explicitly, this means that for each pair of values $x = \xi$, $t = \tau$ and for every positive number ε there exists a positive number δ such that $\rho(x, \xi) < \delta$ and $| t - \tau | < \delta$ imply

$$\rho[\varphi_t(x), \varphi_\tau(\xi)] < \varepsilon. \tag{1}$$

The family φ_t will also be referred to as a *continuous deformation* of the mapping φ_0 into the mapping φ_1. Two continuous mappings φ and ψ of the space P into the space Q will be said to be *homotopic* or *equivalent*, $\varphi \sim \psi$, if there exists a continuous deformation φ_t of φ into ψ, i.e., if there is a continuous family φ_t of mappings of P into Q for which $\varphi_0 = \varphi$ and $\varphi_1 = \psi$.

We shall show that the homotopy relation is reflexive, symmetric, and transitive, and hence is an equivalence relation. It thus serves to partition all continuous mappings of P into Q into equivalence or homotopy classes.

Reflexiveness. If φ is a continuous mapping of P into Q, let $\varphi_t = \varphi$. Then obviously φ_t is a continuous family of mappings and $\varphi_0 = \varphi$, $\varphi_1 = \varphi$. Hence $\varphi \sim \varphi$.

Symmetry. If φ and ψ are two continuous mappings of P into Q and $\varphi \sim \psi$, then there exists a continuous family φ_t of mappings of P into Q such that $\varphi_0 = \varphi$ and $\varphi_1 = \psi$. Setting $\psi_t = \varphi_{1-t}$, it is clear that ψ_t is again a continuous family of mappings of P into Q, with $\psi_0 = \psi$ and $\psi_1 = \varphi$. Hence $\psi \sim \varphi$.

Transitivity. Let φ, ψ, ω be three continuous mappings of P into Q such that $\varphi \sim \psi$ and $\psi \sim \omega$, i.e., there exist continuous families φ_t and ψ_t such that $\varphi_0 = \varphi$, $\varphi_1 = \psi$, $\psi_0 = \psi$, $\psi_1 = \omega$. Set

$$\omega_t = \varphi_{2t}, \ 0 \leqq t \leqq \tfrac{1}{2}, \text{ and } \omega_t = \psi_{2t-1}, \ \tfrac{1}{2} \leqq t \leqq 1.$$

There is no contradiction at $t = \frac{1}{2}$, since $\omega_{1/2} = \varphi_1 = \psi_0 = \psi$. The continuity of the family ω_t is an immediate consequence of the continuity of φ_t and ψ_t. Moreover, $\omega_0 = \varphi$, $\omega_1 = \omega$, and hence $\varphi \sim \omega$.

The following elementary construction yields a simple example of a continuous deformation.

A) Let φ and ψ be two continuous mappings of a metric space P into a convex set C of the Euclidean space R^n. In particular, C may be a simplex. Setting

$$\varphi_t(x) = (1 - t)\varphi(x) + t\psi(x),$$

the continuity of the family φ_t follows easily from that of φ and ψ. Since C is convex, φ_t is a mapping of P into C, $0 \leqq t \leqq 1$, and in addition,

$$\varphi_0 = \varphi, \varphi_1 = \psi.$$

Hence any two mappings of a metric space P into a convex set C are homotopic. This solves completely the problem of classifying the mappings of an arbitrary metric space into a convex set.

The following theorem affords an important example of the equivalence of mappings.

THEOREM 19. *If φ is a continuous mapping of a complex K into a complex L satisfying the star condition* (see Theorem 10) *and f is a simplicial approximation to φ of K into L, then the mappings f and φ of the polyhedron $|K|$ into the polyhedron $|L|$ (or equivalently, of the complex K into the complex L) are homotopic.*

Proof. Let L be imbedded in the Euclidean space R^n, so that φ and f are two continuous mappings of $|K|$ into R^n. Setting

$$\varphi_t(x) = (1 - t)\varphi(x) + tf(x),$$

it is clear that φ_t is a continuous family of mappings of $|K|$ into R^n, with $\varphi_0 = \varphi$, $\varphi_1 = f$. It remains to be shown that $\varphi_t(x)$ is contained in $|L|$. If, for a given point $x \in |K|$, D is a simplex of L such that $\varphi(x) \in D$, then, according to Theorem 10, the point $f(x)$ is also in D. Hence, since D is convex, the point $\varphi_t(x)$, as a point of the segment $(\varphi(x), f(x))$, is likewise in D. This proves Theorem 19.

Theorem 19 is important, because it shows that every continuous mapping of a complex K into a complex L is homotopic to a simplicial mapping of some subdivision K^α of K into L. Hence every homotopy class of continuous mappings contains simplicial mappings.

The function $\varphi_t(x)$ which occurs in the study of continuous deformations is a function of two variables, and it is therefore natural to write it in the form customary for two variables, $\varphi_t(x) = \varphi(x, t)$. On the other hand, the notion of the direct product of metric spaces enables one to regard the pair of variables x, t as a point of a new metric space, and at the same time to replace the continuous family of mappings by a single continuous mapping. The significance of the notion of direct product in topology is, of course, not exhausted by this simple application to the problem at hand.

DEFINITION 24. The *direct (topological) product* of two metric spaces R and S is defined to be the space $R \cdot S$ whose points $z = x \cdot y$ are arbitrary pairs x, y, $x \in R$, $y \in S$, and whose topology is defined by the metric

$$\rho(z, z')^2 = \rho(x, x')^2 + \rho(y, y')^2, \tag{2}$$

where $z = x \cdot y$, $z' = x' \cdot y'$ are any two points of $R \cdot S$. It is easily verified that $R \cdot S$ is indeed a metric space (see Notation, H)). In particular, if R and S are Euclidean spaces of dimension r and s, then the product $R \cdot S$ is the Euclidean space of dimension $r + s$. It is readily seen that if φ and ψ are homeomorphisms of R onto R^* and S onto S^*, respectively, then the mapping which assigns the point $\varphi(x) \cdot \psi(y)$ to the point $x \cdot y$ is a homeomorphism of $R \cdot S$ onto $R^* \cdot S^*$. Thus the notion of direct product is topologically invariant.

We shall now apply the concept of direct product to the problem of continuous deformations.

B) Let φ_t be a continuous family of mappings of a metric space P into a metric space Q and denote by J the segment $0 \leqq t \leqq 1$ of the real line (J is obviously a metric space). Setting $\Phi(z) = \Phi(x \cdot t) = \varphi_t(x)$, $z = x \cdot t$, the function Φ assigns to each point $z \in P \cdot J$ the point $\Phi(z) \in Q$, and is a continuous mapping of $P \cdot J$ into Q. Conversely, if Ψ is an arbitrary continuous mapping of $P \cdot J$ into Q, and $\psi_t(x) = \Psi(x \cdot t) = \Psi(z)$, $x \cdot t = z$, then ψ_t is a continuous family of mappings of P into Q.

We shall show first that the continuity of Φ follows from that of the family φ_t. Let ε be a positive number and choose $\delta > 0$ so that

$$\rho[\varphi_t(x), \varphi_\tau(\xi)] < \varepsilon$$

for $\rho(x, \xi) < \delta$ and $| t - \tau | < \delta$ (see Def. 23). Now if $\rho(x \cdot t, \xi \cdot \tau) < \delta$, then by (2),

$$\rho(x, \xi) < \delta, \qquad | t - \tau | < \delta, \tag{3}$$

whence by (1),

$$\rho[\Phi(x \cdot t), \Phi(\xi \cdot \tau)] = \rho[\varphi_t(x), \varphi_\tau(\xi)] < \varepsilon.$$

Let us now prove that the continuity of Ψ implies that of the family ψ_t. Since Ψ is continuous, given a point $\xi \cdot \tau$ and a positive ε, there exists a positive $\delta' = \delta\sqrt{2}$ such that $\rho(x \cdot t, \xi \cdot \tau) < \delta'$ implies

$$\rho[\Psi(x \cdot t), \Psi(\xi \cdot \tau)] < \varepsilon. \tag{4}$$

If now $\rho(x, \xi) < \delta$, $| t - \tau | < \delta$, then by (2),

$$\rho(x \cdot t, \xi \cdot \tau) < \delta',$$

whence by (4),

$$\rho[\psi_t(x), \psi_\tau(\xi)] = \rho[\Psi(x \cdot t), \Psi(\xi \cdot \tau)] < \varepsilon.$$

This proves B).

§14. The cylinder construction

In this section we shall consider the direct product of a polyhedron $| K |$ by a segment J, and we shall show that $| K | \cdot J$ is a polyhedron. Any definite subdivision of $| K | \cdot J$ into simplexes will be denoted by $K \cdot J$; thus $K \cdot J$ is a complex uniquely defined by the complex K, and

$$| K \cdot J | = | K | \cdot J.$$

In addition, we shall investigate some of the homology properties of $K \cdot J$. The role of the direct product of a space by the segment J has already been indicated in the preceding section; its significance will be completely brought out in the sequel.

Geometry of the Cylinder

A) Let F be any subset of the Euclidean space R^m. We shall regard R^m as imbedded in the Euclidean space R^{m+1} and we shall denote by e a unit vector of R^{m+1} orthogonal to R^m. If J is the set of all numbers t, $0 \leqq t \leqq 1$, the set of all points of the form $z = x + te$, $x \in F$, $t \in J$, is evidently isometric to the direct product $F \cdot J$, and for this reason, it will also be denoted by $F \cdot J$. It is natural to call the set $F \cdot J$ a cylinder constructed on F. The set $F \cdot 0$ will be referred to as the lower, and the set $F \cdot 1$ as the upper, base of the cylinder. If F is a convex set of R^m, then $F \cdot J$ is a convex set of R^{m+1} (see §1, G)). Furthermore, if $F = W$ is a convex body of R^m with frontier V, then $W \cdot J$ is a convex body of R^{m+1} with frontier $V \cdot J \cup W \cdot 0 \cup W \cdot 1$. Hence the frontier of the convex body $W \cdot J$ consists of a lateral surface $V \cdot J$ and two bases $W \cdot 0$ and $W \cdot 1$.

Let us assume that F is convex and show that $F \cdot J$ is also convex. If

$$z_p = x_p + t_p e, \qquad x_p \in F,\ t_p \in J,\ p = 1, 2,$$

are two points of $F \cdot J$, then the point $z = \alpha z_1 + \beta z_2$ of the segment (z_1, z_2) can be written in the form

$$z = \alpha x_1 + \beta x_2 + (\alpha t_1 + \beta t_2)e, \tag{1}$$

where $\alpha \geqq 0$, $\beta \geqq 0$, $\alpha + \beta = 1$. Since F is convex, the point $\alpha x_1 + \beta x_2$ is in F and $t_1 \in J$, $t_2 \in J$ immediately implies $\alpha t_1 + \beta t_2 \in J$.

Now consider the convex body $F = W$. Since W is compact, it follows immediately that $W \cdot J$ is compact. Let us further denote by U the set of all interior points of W and show that if $x_0 \in U$, $0 < t_0 < 1$, then

$$z_0 = x_0 + t_0 e$$

is an interior point of the convex set $W \cdot J$. Since x_0 is an interior point of W, there exists a positive ε such that $x \in R^m$ and $\rho(x, x_0) < \varepsilon$ imply $x \in W$. If necessary, ε can be decreased so that $|t - t_0| < \varepsilon$ implies $0 < t < 1$. If $z = x + te$, then $\rho(z, z_0) < \varepsilon$ implies $\rho(x, x_0) < \varepsilon$ and $|t - t_0| < \varepsilon$, whence $z \in W \cdot J$, and z_0 is an interior point of $W \cdot J$.

If now $z_0 = x_0 + t_0 e$ is a point of $W \cdot J$ on the lateral surface $V \cdot J$ of the cylinder $W \cdot J$, i.e., $x_0 \in V$, then we shall show that z_0 is a frontier point of $W \cdot J$. Since x_0 is a frontier point of W, there exists a point $x \in R^m$ arbitrarily near x_0 and not in W. Hence the point $z = x + t_0 e$ is not in $W \cdot J$ and is arbitrarily near z_0, which means that z_0 is a frontier point of $W \cdot J$. Let $z_0 = x_0 + 0 \cdot e$ be any point of the lower base of the cylinder $W \cdot J$; then there is a point $z = x_0 - \varepsilon e$, not in $W \cdot J$, in an arbitrary neighborhood of z_0, whence z_0 is a frontier point of $W \cdot J$. Similarly, if $z_0 = x_0 + 1 \cdot e$ is a point of the upper base, there is a point $x_0 + (1 + \varepsilon)e$, in an arbitrary neighborhood of z_0, which is not contained in $W \cdot J$, so that z_0 is a frontier point of $W \cdot J$ in this case also. This proves A).

B) Let $F = A^r = (a_0, a_1, \cdots, a_r)$ be a simplex of the Euclidean space R^m, $R^m \subset R^{m+1}$, and e a unit vector orthogonal to R^m (see A)). The cylinder $A^r \cdot J = P^{r+1}$ will be called a prism. Denote the set of all proper faces of the simplex A^r by S and define the lateral surface of the prism P^{r+1} to be $|S| \cdot J$. The complete frontier of the prism P^{r+1} is defined to be

$$|S| \cdot J \cup A^r \cdot 0 \cup A^r \cdot 1 = Q^r.$$

The points of the prism P^{r+1} which are not contained in its frontier Q^r will be called the interior points of the prism. One of the interior points of the prism is the center $\sigma + \frac{1}{2}e$ of P^{r+1} (where σ is the center of the simplex A^r). If κ is an interior point of P^{r+1}, κ is in general position with respect to Q^r (see §8, A)), and $\kappa(Q^r) = P^{r+1}$.

If $x = \lambda^0 a_0 + \cdots + \lambda^r a_r$ is any point of the simplex A^r, then the point $z = x + te$ of the prism P^{r+1} is uniquely determined by the numbers $\lambda^0, \lambda^1, \cdots, \lambda^r, t$, which will be called the intrinsic coordinates of the point z of P^{r+1}. It is clear that the point z is an interior point of P^{r+1} if, and only if, all the corresponding numbers λ^i are positive and t satisfies the inequality $0 < t < 1$. Thus the property of being an interior or a frontier point is formulated in terms of the intrinsic coordinates of the point.

If $x_p = \lambda^0{}_p a_0 + \cdots + \lambda^r{}_p a_r$, $p = 1, 2$, are two points of A^r, then (1) can be rewritten in the form

(2) $$z = (\alpha\lambda^0{}_1 + \beta\lambda^0{}_2)a_0 + \cdots + (\alpha\lambda^r{}_1 + \beta\lambda^r{}_2)a_r + (\alpha t_1 + \beta t_2)e,$$

or alternatively

(3) $$\lambda^0 = \alpha\lambda^0{}_1 + \beta\lambda^0{}_2, \cdots, \lambda^r = \alpha\lambda^r{}_1 + \beta\lambda^r{}_2, \quad t = \alpha t_1 + \beta t_2.$$

Thus the property that a point lie on the segment (z_1, z_2) is expressed in terms of the intrinsic coordinates of the prism.

In view of the above, it suffices to prove the assertions in B) for a single arbitrary r-simplex; and in particular, we may assume that $m = r$, i.e., that A^r lies in the r-dimensional Euclidean space R^r. With this condition, A^r is a convex body in R^r (see §8, B)), whence by A), P^{r+1} is a convex body of R^{r+1}, where the frontier Q^r of the prism P^{r+1} is now the frontier of the convex body P^{r+1}. The assertions in B) have already been proved, however, for a convex body P^{r+1} and its frontier Q^r (see §8, (1)).

Let us now construct the complex $K \cdot J$ by subdividing the space $|K| \cdot J$ into simplexes. The set $|K| \cdot J$ consists of the prisms $A^r \cdot J = P^{r+1}$, where A^r is a simplex of K; hence, in order to subdivide $|K| \cdot J$ into simplexes, it is necessary to indicate how the prisms P^{r+1} are to be subdivided. If $r = 0$, the prism P^1 is a segment, i.e., a 1-simplex, and does not need to be subdivided. If $r > 0$, S is an $(r - 1)$-complex and the complex $S \cdot J$ can be regarded as already defined. Let the two simplexes $A^r \cdot 0$ and $A^r \cdot 1$ be adjoined to the complex $S \cdot J$, and denote the resulting complex by C^r. Then $|C^r| = Q^r$, and in view of B) we can construct the complex $\kappa(C^r)$, where κ is the center of the prism P^{r+1}. The set of simplexes of the complex $\kappa(C^r)$ constitutes a subdivision of the prism P^{r+1}. Such, in general terms, is the construction of the complex $K \cdot J$, and we now turn to its formal description.

C) Let K be a complex imbedded in the Euclidean space $R^m \subset R^{m+1}$ (see A), B)). With the complex K associate the completely determined complex $K \cdot J$ imbedded in R^{m+1}, which will be called the cylinder over the complex K.

If A is an arbitrary simplex of K, denote by $K \cdot 0$ the set of all simplexes of the form $A \cdot 0$ and by $K \cdot 1$ the set of all simplexes of the form $A \cdot 1$. It is clear that $K \cdot 0$ and $K \cdot 1$ are complexes. If K is a 0-complex, define the complex $K \cdot J$ as the set of all simplexes contained in $K \cdot 0$ and $K \cdot 1$ and all segments of the form $a \cdot J$, where a is a vertex of K. Now assume that the complex $K \cdot J$ has already been defined for an n-complex K, so as to satisfy the following conditions: a) $|K \cdot J| = |K| \cdot J$; b) if L is a subcomplex of K, then $L \cdot J$ is a subcomplex of $K \cdot J$; c) $K \cdot 0$ and $K \cdot 1$ are subcomplexes of $K \cdot J$. In order to define the complex $K \cdot J$ for an $(n + 1)$-complex K, denote by M the n-skeleton of K, and by $A_1^{n+1}, \cdots, A_k^{n+1}$ the set of all

$(n + 1)$-simplexes of K. In addition, denote the set of all proper faces of the simplex A_i^{n+1} by S_i and the center of the prism $P_i = A_i^{n+1} \cdot J$ by κ_i. Adjoin the simplexes $A_i^{n+1} \cdot 0$ and $A_i^{n+1} \cdot 1$ to the complex $S_i \cdot J$ and denote the resulting complex by C_i. If $K \cdot J$ is the set of all simplexes contained in the complexes $M \cdot J$ and $\kappa_i(C_i)$, $i = 1, 2, \cdots, k$, then $K \cdot J$ is a complex for which conditions a), b), and c) are satisfied.

In order not to have to repeat the same proofs for the complexes $K \cdot 0$ and $K \cdot 1$, let p be 0 or 1 in the sequel.

We shall first show that if $P \in M \cdot J$, then

(4) *the simplexes P and $A_i^{n+1} \cdot p$ are properly situated.*

Now, $P \subset | M \cdot J | = | M | \cdot J$, whence

$$(5) \qquad \begin{aligned} P \cap (A_i^{n+1} \cdot p) \subset (| M | \cdot J) \cap (A_i^{n+1} \cdot p) \subset (| M | \cdot p) \cap (A_i^{n+1} \cdot p) \\ = | S_i | \cdot p. \end{aligned}$$

Since $S_i \cdot p$ is a subcomplex of the complex $M \cdot p$ and the latter, by c), is a subcomplex of $M \cdot J$, it follows that $S_i \cdot p$ is a subcomplex of $M \cdot J$. Let $a_0 \cdot p, \cdots, a_r \cdot p$ be the set of all vertices of the simplex $P \in M \cdot J$ which are contained in the subcomplex $S_i \cdot p$ of $M \cdot J$. The points $a_0, \cdots, a_r$ are vertices of the simplex A_i^{n+1}; denote by D the face of A_i^{n+1} which spans them. The face $D \cdot p$ is common to both simplexes P and $A_i^{n+1} \cdot p$, so that to prove (4) it suffices to show that

$$(6) \qquad P \cap (A_i^{n+1} \cdot p) = D \cdot p.$$

If the equality $D = A_i^{n+1}$ were to hold, relation (6) would be true. This, however, is incompatible with (5). Hence we need consider only the case that D is a proper face of A_i^{n+1}, and is consequently contained in the complex S_i. By (5), in order to prove (6), it suffices to show that

$$(7) \qquad P \cap (| S_i | \cdot p) = D \cdot p.$$

Let E be any simplex of S_i. Since P and $E \cdot p$ are simplexes of a single complex $M \cdot J$, the intersection of P with $E \cdot p$ is a simplex spanning the common vertices of P and $E \cdot p$. The vertices common to P and $S_i \cdot p$ are, however, all contained in the simplex $D \cdot p$, whence $P \cap E \cdot p \subset D \cdot p$. This proves (7), which implies (6) and then (4).

Relation (4) implies that C_i is a complex. Indeed, C_i is obtained by adjoining both simplexes $A_i^{n+1} \cdot p$, $p = 0, 1$, to the complex $S_i \cdot J$. The simplexes $A_i^{n+1} \cdot 0$ and $A_i^{n+1} \cdot 1$ are disjoint, and hence are properly situated. Furthermore, if $P \in S_i \cdot J$, then by b), $P \in M \cdot J$, whence it follows from (4) that the simplexes P and $A_i^{n+1} \cdot p$ are properly situated. Thus C_i satisfies condition 2) of Def. 5. It also satisfies condition 1), since all the proper faces of the simplex $A_i^{n+1} \cdot p$ are contained in $S_i \cdot p$, and the latter, by c), is a subcomplex of $S_i \cdot J$. Hence $\kappa_i(C_i)$ is a complex (see B) and §8, D)).

Since $K \cdot J$ was defined as a set of simplexes contained in several complexes, it obviously satisfies 1) of Def. 5. To show that it also satisfies 2), let P and Q be two simplexes of $K \cdot J$ and consider three different cases.

Case 1. If P and Q are both in $M \cdot J$, they are properly situated, since $M \cdot J$ is a complex.

Case 2. If $P \in M \cdot J$, $Q \in \kappa_i(C_i)$, then, since all simplexes of the complex $\kappa_i(C_i)$ are faces of simplexes of the form $\kappa_i(B)$, $B \in C_i$, we can assume that $Q = \kappa_i(B)$. Now $P \subset |M| \cdot J$, $Q = \kappa_i(B) \subset |\kappa_i(C_i)| = P_i = A_i^{n+1} \cdot J$, whence $P \cap Q \subset (|M| \cdot J) \cap (A_i^{n+1} \cdot J) = |S_i| \cdot J \subset |C_i|$. Moreover, since $\kappa_i(B) \cap |C_i| = B$, it follows that $P \cap Q \subset P \cap B$. If $B = A_i^{n+1} \cdot p$, then (4) implies that P and B are properly situated, and hence P and Q are also properly situated (see §2, D)). If $B \in S_i \cdot J \subset M \cdot J$, then P and B are properly situated, since they are simplexes of the same complex $M \cdot J$, and again P and Q are properly situated (see §2, D)).

Case 3. If $P \in \kappa_i(C_i)$, $Q \in \kappa_j(C_j)$ and $i = j$, then P and Q are properly situated since they belong to the same complex. If $i \neq j$, then as in Case 2, we can assume that $P = \kappa_i(A)$, $A \in C_i$, $Q = \kappa_j(B)$, $B \in C_j$. Since $i \neq j$, it follows readily that $P \cap Q \subset |C_i| \cap |C_j|$, and since $\kappa_i(A) \cap |C_i| = A$ and $\kappa_j(B) \cap |C_j| = B$, it also follows that $P \cap Q \subset A \cap B$. If $A = A_i^{n+1} \cdot p$, $B = A_j^{n+1} \cdot p'$, then A and B are obviously properly situated, since either they do not intersect at all for $p \neq p'$ or they are contained in a single complex $K \cdot p$ for $p = p'$. If $A \in S_i \cdot J$ and $B = A_j^{n+1} \cdot p$, then Case 3 reduces to (4). If $A \in S_i \cdot J$, $B \in S_j \cdot J$, then A and B are both contained in $M \cdot J$, and hence are properly situated. Thus A and B are always properly situated, which implies that P and Q are properly situated. Hence $K \cdot J$ is a complex (see §2, D)).

To prove a), note that $|K \cdot J| = |M \cdot J| \cup |\kappa_1(C_1)| \cup \cdots \cup |\kappa_k(C_k)|$ and $|K| \cdot J = |M| \cdot J \cup P_1 \cup \cdots \cup P_k$. By the inductive hypothesis, $|M \cdot J| = |M| \cdot J$. Moreover, $|C_i|$ consists of the set of all frontier points of the prism P_i (see B)), since, again by the inductive hypothesis,

$$|S_i \cdot J| = |S_i| \cdot J$$

is the lateral surface of the prism P_i. Hence $|\kappa_i(C_i)| = \kappa_i(|C_i|) = P_i$, so that $|K \cdot J| = |K| \cdot J$.

In order to prove b), let L be a subcomplex of K, N the n-skeleton of L, and $A_1^{n+1}, \cdots, A_l^{n+1}$ the set of all $(n+1)$-simplexes of L, $l \leq k$. By the inductive hypothesis, $N \cdot J$ is a subcomplex of $M \cdot J$ and $L \cdot J$ consists of all the simplexes contained in the complexes $N \cdot J$ and $\kappa_j(C_j)$, $j = 1, \cdots, l$, while K is the set of all simplexes of the complexes $M \cdot J$ and

$$\kappa_i(C_i), \; i = 1, \cdots, k.$$

Hence $L \cdot J$ is a subcomplex of $K \cdot J$.

We shall now prove c). The complex $K \cdot p$ obviously consists of all the simplexes of the complex $M \cdot p$ and of the simplexes $A_l^{n+1} \cdot p$, $l = 1, \cdots, k$. By the inductive hypothesis, $M \cdot p$ is a subcomplex of $M \cdot J \subset K \cdot J$ and the simplex $A_i^{n+1} \cdot p$ is in the complex $\kappa_i(C_i)$; hence $K \cdot p$ is a subcomplex of $K \cdot J$.

It is clear that the dimension of the complex $K \cdot J$ is one greater than that of K.

Algebra of the Cylinder

Having constructed the complex $K \cdot J$, let us now associate with each r-chain x of K an $(r + 1)$-chain $x \cdot J$ of $K \cdot J$ over the same coefficient group as the chain x.

D) Let K be a complex, $K \cdot J$ the cylinder over K (see C)), and p either 0 or 1. To the oriented simplex $A^r = \varepsilon\,(a_0, \cdots, a_r)$ of K assign the oriented r-simplex $A^r \cdot p = \varepsilon\,(a_0 \cdot p, \cdots, a_r \cdot p)$ of $K \cdot p$, and if $x = g_1 A^r{}_1 + \cdots + g_k A^r{}_k$ is any r-chain of K, set

$$x \cdot p = g_1(A^r{}_1 \cdot p) + \cdots + g_k(A^r{}_k \cdot p).$$

The boundary of $x \cdot p$ satisfies the relation

$$\Delta(x \cdot p) = (\Delta x) \cdot p. \tag{8}$$

We shall now construct the chain $x \cdot J$.

E) Let K be a complex, $K \cdot J$ the cylinder over K (see C)), and

$$x = g_1 A^r{}_1 + \cdots + g_k A^r{}_k$$

any r-chain of K over the coefficient group G. Assign to the chain x the $(r + 1)$-chain $x \cdot J$ of $K \cdot J$ over G, referred to as the cylinder constructed on x, in the following way. If $A^r{}_i \cdot J$ has already been constructed for the simplest integral chain, an oriented simplex $A^r{}_i$, then set

$$x \cdot J = g_1(A^r{}_1 \cdot J) + \cdots + g_k(A^r{}_k \cdot J). \tag{9}$$

The chain $A^r{}_i \cdot J$ is constructed by induction on the dimension r. If

$$A^0 = +(a)$$

is an oriented 0-simplex, there is a segment $a \cdot J$ in the complex $K \cdot J$ with endpoints $a \cdot 0$ and $a \cdot 1$. Orient this segment in the direction from $a \cdot 0$ to $a \cdot 1$ and take it to be $A^0 \cdot J$, i.e., set $A^0 \cdot J = +(a \cdot 0, a \cdot 1)$. The boundary of $A^0 \cdot J$ is

$$\Delta(A^0 \cdot J) = +(a \cdot 1) - (a \cdot 0) = A^0 \cdot 1 - A^0 \cdot 0,$$

whence (9) implies

$$\Delta(x^0 \cdot J) = x^0 \cdot 1 - x^0 \cdot 0 \tag{10}$$

for any 0-chain x^0.

Now assume that the cylinder construction has already been defined for any n-chain, so as to satisfy the condition

$$\Delta(x \cdot J) = x \cdot 1 - x \cdot 0 - (\Delta x) \cdot J. \tag{11}$$

Note that (11) reduces to (10) if $n = 0$. In order to define the cylinder for an $(n + 1)$-chain, denote by $A_1^{n+1}, \cdots, A_k^{n+1}$ the set of all arbitrarily oriented $(n + 1)$-simplexes of K, and, for the rest, retain the notation used in C). The chain ΔA_i^{n+1} is n-dimensional and consists of simplexes of the complex S_i. Hence the chain $(\Delta A_i^{n+1}) \cdot J$ composed of simplexes of the complex $S_i \cdot J$ is defined. Now form the chain

$$u_i = A_i^{n+1} \cdot 1 - A_i^{n+1} \cdot 0 - (\Delta A_i^{n+1}) \cdot J,$$

which is contained in the complex C_i. The cone $\kappa_i(u_i)$ is therefore a chain of the complex $\kappa_i(C_i)$ (see §8, E)), and we may set

$$A_i^{n+1} \cdot J = \kappa_i(u_i) = \kappa_i(A_i^{n+1} \cdot 1 - A_i^{n+1} \cdot 0 - (\Delta A_i^{n+1}) \cdot J). \tag{12}$$

If we now define the cylinder $x \cdot J$ for any $(n + 1)$-chain x in accordance with (9), then relation (11) is again satisfied.

It suffices to prove (11) for the simplest $(n + 1)$-chain $x = A_i^{n+1}$. Since (11) holds for the n-chain ΔA_i^{n+1} by the inductive hypothesis, it follows that

$$\begin{aligned} \Delta[(\Delta A_i^{n+1}) \cdot J] &= (\Delta A_i^{n+1}) \cdot 1 - (\Delta A_i^{n+1}) \cdot 0 - (\Delta\Delta A_i^{n+1}) \cdot J \\ &= (\Delta A_i^{n+1}) \cdot 1 - (\Delta A_i^{n+1}) \cdot 0, \end{aligned} \tag{13}$$

whence (8) and (13) yield

$$\Delta u_i = (\Delta A_i^{n+1}) \cdot 1 - (\Delta A_i^{n+1}) \cdot 0 - \Delta[(\Delta A_i^{n+1}) \cdot J] = 0. \tag{14}$$

The boundary of the chain $\kappa_i(u_i) = A_i^{n+1} \cdot J$ is computed on the basis of §8, (11), i.e.,

$$\begin{aligned} \Delta(A_i^{n+1} \cdot J) = \Delta\kappa_i(u_i) = u_i - \kappa_i(\Delta u_i) &= u_i \\ &= A_i^{n+1} \cdot 1 - A_i^{n+1} \cdot 0 - (\Delta A_i^{n+1}) \cdot J. \end{aligned}$$

Hence (11) holds for $x = A_i^{n+1}$.

A consequence of relation (11) is the basic proposition:

F) If z is a cycle of K, then the cycles $z \cdot 1$ and $z \cdot 0$ are homologous in $K \cdot J$.

Indeed, if $\Delta z = 0$, then (11) implies

$$\Delta(z \cdot J) = z \cdot 1 - z \cdot 0, \quad \text{i.e.,} \quad z \cdot 1 \sim z \cdot 0 \quad \text{in } K \cdot J.$$

§15. Homology invariants of continuous mappings

In this section we shall associate with every continuous mapping ω of a polyhedron P into a polyhedron Q homomorphisms of the corresponding Betti groups, and prove that two homotopic mappings induce identical homomorphisms. This is the central result of the whole homology theory of continuous mappings.

Homomorphisms for Complexes

LEMMA 1. *If f_0 and f_1 are two homotopic simplicial mappings of a complex K into a complex L, and z is any cycle of K, then $\hat{f}_0(z) \sim \hat{f}_1(z)$, i.e., the induced homomorphisms $\tilde{f}_0$ and $\tilde{f}_1$ of the group $B^r(K)$ into the group $B^r(L)$ are identical.*

Proof. Let f_t be a continuous family of mappings of K into L which deforms f_0 into f_1, and set $f(x, t) = f_t(x)$, $x \in |K|$, $t \in J$, as in §13, B). Then f is a continuous mapping of $K \cdot J$ into L. The mapping f is not simplicial on the whole complex $K \cdot J$, but it is simplicial on the subcomplexes $K \cdot 0$ and $K \cdot 1$, since f_0 and f_1 are simplicial. Hence the chain mapping $\hat{f}$ is defined for chains of $K \cdot 0$ and $K \cdot 1$, and by definition,

$$\hat{f}_0(z) = \hat{f}(z \cdot 0), \quad \hat{f}_1(z) = \hat{f}(z \cdot 1), \tag{1}$$

where z any cycle of K.

Let $(K \cdot J)^\alpha$ be a subdivision of the complex $K \cdot J$ so fine that there is a simplicial approximation g to f of $(K \cdot J)^\alpha$ into L. Since $z \cdot 0 \sim z \cdot 1$ in $K \cdot J$ (see §14, F)), it follows that $(z \cdot 0)^\alpha \sim (z \cdot 1)^\alpha$ in $(K \cdot J)^\alpha$ (see §9, E)); whence, in virtue of §7, F),

$$\hat{g}[(z \cdot 0)^\alpha] \sim \hat{g}[(z \cdot 1)^\alpha]. \tag{2}$$

Since g approximates f on $(K \cdot J)^\alpha$, it does so also on any subcomplex of $(K \cdot J)^\alpha$, in particular, on $(K \cdot 0)^\alpha$. Hence, by the lemma of §12,

$$\hat{g}[(z \cdot 0)^\alpha] = \hat{f}(z \cdot 0), \tag{3}$$

and similarly,

$$\hat{g}[(z \cdot 1)^\alpha] = \hat{f}(z \cdot 1). \tag{4}$$

Comparison of (1), (2), (3), and (4) yields

$$\hat{f}_0(z) \sim \hat{f}_1(z).$$

This proves Lemma 1.

LEMMA 2. *Let K and L be two complexes, K^α and K^β two subdivisions of K, L^α and L^β two subdivisions of L, and f^α and f^β simplicial mappings of K^α into L^α and K^β into L^β, respectively. If f^α and f^β are homotopic, then the induced homomorphisms $\bar{f}^\alpha$ and $\bar{f}^\beta$ of $B^r(K)$ into $B^r(L)$* (see §12, A)) *are identical.*

Proof. Let K^γ be the finer of the two subdivisions K^α and K^β and let L^γ be the coarser of the subdivisions L^α and L^β. Then K^γ is a subdivision of K^α and K^β, while L^α and L^β are subdivisions of L^γ.

The indices α and β are interchangeable in the discussion; in the sequel, the construction will be carried out for the index α, but it should be kept in mind that it applies equally well to the index β.

Let e be the identity mapping of K^α onto itself, and e^α a simplicial approximation to e of K^γ into K^α. By Theorem 19, there is a continuous family e_t which deforms e into e^α. Similarly, let g be the identity mapping of L^γ onto itself, g^α a simplicial approximation to g of L^α into L^γ, and g_t a continuous family which deforms g into g^α. This system of mappings may be represented by the following scheme:

$$L^\gamma \underset{g^\alpha}{\overset{g}{\leftarrow}} L^\alpha \underset{f^\alpha}{\overset{f^\alpha}{\leftarrow}} K^\alpha \underset{e^\alpha}{\overset{e}{\leftarrow}} K^\gamma,$$

where the arrows refer to the mappings, the initial mappings are written above the arrows and their simplicial approximations below. We may regard f^α as a simplicial approximation to itself. It is easily seen that the family of mappings $g_t f^\alpha e_t$ of K^γ into L^γ is continuous, and since

$$g_0 f^\alpha e_0 = f^\alpha, \; g_1 f^\alpha e_1 = g^\alpha f^\alpha e^\alpha,$$

it follows that

$$f^\alpha \sim g^\alpha f^\alpha e^\alpha. \tag{5}$$

The simplicial mappings induce homomorphisms of the Betti groups which can be represented schematically as follows:

$$B^r(L^\gamma) \underset{\bar{g}^\alpha}{\leftarrow} B^r(L^\alpha) \underset{\bar{f}^\alpha}{\leftarrow} B^r(K^\alpha) \underset{\bar{e}^\alpha}{\leftarrow} B^r(K^\gamma),$$

$$B^r(L) \leftarrow B^r(L) \leftarrow B^r(K) \leftarrow B^r(K),$$

where the homomorphisms induced in the Betti groups of the subdivided complexes are written on the first line and the homomorphisms of the Betti groups of the initial complexes appear on the second line. The latter were defined in §12, A). Since g^α is an approximation to the identity mapping, the homomorphism $\tilde{g}^\alpha$ of $B^r(L)$ into $B^r(L)$ induced by it is, in virtue of §12, D), the identity. Similarly, $\tilde{e}^\alpha$ is the identity homomorphism of $B^r(K)$ onto itself, whence the homomorphisms satisfy the relation

$$\tilde{f}^\alpha = \tilde{g}^\alpha \tilde{f}^\alpha \tilde{e}^\alpha. \tag{6}$$

Application of the above argument to the index β yields the equivalence

$$f^\beta \sim g^\beta f^\beta e^\beta \tag{7}$$

for the continuous mappings and the equality

$$\tilde{f}^\beta = \tilde{g}^\beta \tilde{f}^\beta \tilde{e}^\beta \tag{8}$$

for the homomorphisms.

By hypothesis, $f^\alpha \sim f^\beta$, whence (5) and (7) imply

$$g^\alpha f^\alpha e^\alpha \sim g^\beta f^\beta e^\beta. \tag{9}$$

Since $g^\alpha f^\alpha e^\alpha$ and $g^\beta f^\beta e^\beta$ are two simplicial mappings of K^γ into L^γ, it follows from Lemma 1 of the present section and §7, G) that

$$\tilde{g}^\alpha \tilde{f}^\alpha \tilde{e}^\alpha = \tilde{g}^\beta \tilde{f}^\beta \tilde{e}^\beta. \tag{10}$$

Comparison of (6), (8), and (10) yields

$$\tilde{f}^\alpha = \tilde{f}^\beta.$$

This proves Lemma 2.

THEOREM 20. *Let φ_0 be a continuous mapping of a complex K into a complex L, L^α any subdivision of L, and K^α a subdivision of K for which there exists a simplicial approximation f^α to φ_0 of K^α into L^α. Then the induced homomorphism $\tilde{f}^\alpha$ of $B^r(K)$ into $B^r(L)$ is independent of the choice of the particular subdivisions K^α and L^α and of the particular approximation f^α, and is determined only by the initial mapping φ_0. Hence we may denote the homomorphism $\tilde{f}^\alpha$ simply by $\tilde{\varphi}_0$, $\tilde{\varphi}_0[B^r(K)] \subset B^r(L)$. In addition, if φ_0 and φ_1 are two homotopic mappings of K into L, their induced homomorphisms $\tilde{\varphi}_0$ and $\tilde{\varphi}_1$ are identical.*

Proof. If L^β is any subdivision of L and K^β is a subdivision of K for which there is a simplicial approximation f^β to φ_1 of K^β into L^β, then, according to Theorem 19, $f^\alpha \sim \varphi_0$, $f^\beta \sim \varphi_1$, and since, by hypothesis, $\varphi_0 \sim \varphi_1$, it follows that $f^\alpha \sim f^\beta$. Hence, by Lemma 2 of this section, the homomorphisms $\tilde{f}^\alpha$ and $\tilde{f}^\beta$ are identical. Since $\tilde{f}^\alpha$ and $\tilde{f}^\beta$ were constructed independently of one another, the homomorphisms $\tilde{\varphi}_0$ and $\tilde{\varphi}_1$ of the theorem are likewise independent of the choice of K^α, K^β, and f^α. This proves Theorem 20.

According to Theorem 20, each continuous mapping φ of K into L induces a homomorphism $\tilde{\varphi}$ of the corresponding Betti groups. We shall prove the following important property of the induced homomorphism.

THEOREM 21. *If K, L, M are three complexes, and* φ *and* θ *are continuous mappings of K into L and L into M, respectively, then the continuous mapping* $\theta\varphi$ *of K into M induces the homomorphism* $\tilde{\theta}\tilde{\varphi}$, *the product of* $\tilde{\theta}$ *and* $\tilde{\varphi}$ (see Theorem 20).

Proof. Let M^α be any subdivision of M and let L^α and K^α be subdivisions of L and K, respectively, so fine that the continuous mappings θ and φ of L^α into M^α and of K^α into L^α admit of simplicial approximations g^α and f^α, respectively. Schematically, we have

$$M^\alpha \underset{g^\alpha}{\overset{\theta}{\longleftarrow}} L^\alpha \underset{f^\alpha}{\overset{\varphi}{\longleftarrow}} K^\alpha,$$

where the arrows refer to the mappings, the initial continuous mappings are written above the arrows, and their simplicial approximations below. By §7, D), $g^\alpha f^\alpha$ is a simplicial approximation to $\theta\varphi$. By Theorem 20,

$$\tilde{\varphi} = \tilde{f}^\alpha, \tilde{\theta} = \tilde{g}^\alpha$$

and $\theta\varphi$ induces the product $\tilde{g}^\alpha\tilde{f}^\alpha$ of the homomorphisms $\tilde{g}^\alpha$ and $\tilde{f}^\alpha$ (see §7, G)). Hence $\theta\varphi$ induces the homomorphism $\tilde{\theta}\tilde{\varphi}$. This proves Theorem 21.

The Homomorphisms of Betti Groups of Polyhedra

THEOREM 22. *Let* ω *be a continuous mapping of a polyhedron P into a polyhedron Q,* ξ *an element of the group* $B^r(P)$ (see Def. 22), (σ, K) *and* (τ, L) *arbitrary triangulations of P and Q, and finally x a representative of the element* ξ *in the triangulation* (σ, K), $x \in B^r(\sigma, K) = B^r(K)$. *The mapping* $\overset{-1}{\tau}\omega\sigma = \mu$ *is obviously a continuous mapping of K into L, which by Theorem 20, induces a homomorphism of* $B^r(K)$ *into* $B^r(L)$. *Set* $y = \tilde{\mu}(x)$ *and denote by* η *the element of* $B^r(Q)$ *which contains y. Then* η *is independent of the choice of the representative x of* ξ *and it is therefore possible to define a homomorphism* $\tilde{\omega}$ *of* $B^r(P)$ *into* $B^r(Q)$ *by setting* $\eta = \tilde{\omega}(\xi)$. *Moreover, if* ω_0 *and* ω_1 *are two homotopic continuous mappings of P into Q, then* $\tilde{\omega}_0$ *and* $\tilde{\omega}_1$ *are identical.*

Proof. Let (σ_1, K_1) and (σ_2, K_2) be any two triangulations of P and (τ_1, L_1), (τ_2, L_2) two arbitrary triangulations of Q. The continuous mappings

$$\overset{-1}{\tau_1}\omega\sigma_1 = \mu_1, \quad \overset{-1}{\tau_2}\omega\sigma_2 = \mu_2, \quad \overset{-1}{\sigma_2}\sigma_1 = \varphi, \quad \overset{-1}{\tau_2}\tau_1 = \theta,$$

obviously satisfy the equality

$$\mu_2 = \theta\mu_1\overset{-1}{\varphi}.$$

By Theorem 21, the same equality holds for the induced homomorphisms:

$$(11) \qquad \tilde{\mu}_2 = \tilde{\theta}\tilde{\mu}_1\overset{-1}{\tilde{\varphi}}.$$

Let ξ be any element of $B^r(P)$ and x_1, x_2 representatives of ξ in $B^r(K_1)$ and $B^r(K_2)$, respectively (see Def. 22). Setting $y_1 = \tilde{\mu}_1(x_1)$, $y_2 = \tilde{\mu}_2(x_2)$, we shall show that y_1 and y_2 are representatives of the same element η of the group $B^r(Q)$ in the groups $B^r(\tau_1, L_1)$ and $B^r(\tau_2, L_2)$. This will prove the first part of Theorem 22.

Since x_1 and x_2 are representatives of the same element ξ, it follows from Def. 22 that $x_1 = \tilde{\varphi}^{-1}(x_2)$, whence, by (11), $y_2 = \tilde{\theta}(y_1)$. This in turn, by Def. 22, implies that y_1 and y_2 are in the same element of $B^r(Q)$.

Now if ω_t is a continuous family of mappings of P into Q, it is readily seen that $\tau^{-1}\omega_t\sigma = \upsilon_t$ is a continuous family of mappings of K into L. Let $\xi \in B^r(P)$ and let x be a representative of the element ξ in the group $B^r(\sigma, K)$. We must show that $\tilde{\omega}_0(\xi) = \tilde{\omega}_1(\xi)$. Since υ_0 and υ_1 are homotopic, Theorem 20 implies that $\tilde{\upsilon}_0(x) = \tilde{\upsilon}_1(x)$, which means that $\tilde{\omega}_0(\xi) = \tilde{\omega}_1(\xi)$. This proves Theorem 22.

THEOREM 23. *If P, Q, R are three polyhedra, φ a continuous mapping of P into Q, and θ a continuous mapping of Q into R, then the continuous mapping $\theta\varphi = \omega$ of P into R induces the homomorphism $\tilde{\omega} = \tilde{\theta}\tilde{\varphi}$, the product of $\tilde{\theta}$ and $\tilde{\varphi}$.*

Proof. Theorem 23 follows immediately from Theorems 21 and 22. Let (ρ, K), (σ, L), and (τ, M) be arbitrary triangulations of P, Q, and R, respectively. The homomorphisms $\tilde{\varphi}$, $\tilde{\theta}$, and $\tilde{\omega}$ are constructed by means of the continuous mappings $\sigma^{-1}\varphi\rho = \lambda$ of K into L, $\tau^{-1}\theta\sigma = \mu$ of L into M, and $\tau^{-1}\theta\varphi\rho = \nu$ of K into M, respectively. Since $\nu = \mu\lambda$, Theorem 23 follows directly from Theorem 21.

Homotopy Types of Polyhedra

The notion of homotopy types of polyhedra (see Def. 25) has lately begun to play an essential role in topology. Due to its close relation to the material presented above, it is discussed here, although it will not be used in the sequel. It is interesting to note that many of the invariants of polyhedra having the same homotopy type are identical. We shall confine ourselves here, however, to a proof of this fact for the Betti groups.

A) If P is a polyhedron and φ is a continuous mapping of P into itself which is homotopic to the identity, then the induced homomorphism $\tilde{\varphi}$ of $B^r(P)$ into itself is the identity.

Because of Theorem 22, we may assume that φ is the identity mapping of P into itself. If (ρ, K) is any triangulation of P, the mapping $\rho^{-1}\varphi\rho = \mu$ of K into itself is the identity. Hence the homomorphism $\tilde{\mu}$ of $B^r(\rho, K)$ into itself is also the identity, and this, by Theorem 22, implies A).

DEFINITION 25. Let P and Q be two polyhedra, and φ and θ continuous mappings of P into Q and Q into P, respectively. The mappings φ and θ are said to be *homotopically inverse* to one another if both mappings, $\theta\varphi$ of P into itself and $\varphi\theta$ of Q into itself, are homotopic to the identity. The polyhedra P and Q are said to have the same *homotopy type* if there exist homotopically inverse mappings φ of P into Q and θ of Q into P.

THEOREM 24. *If two polyhedra P and Q have the same homotopy type and φ and θ are corresponding homotopically inverse mappings* (see Def. 25), *then the induced homomorphisms $\tilde{\varphi}$ and $\tilde{\theta}$ are isomorphisms of $B^r(P)$ onto $B^r(Q)$ and $B^r(Q)$ onto $B^r(P)$, respectively, and $\tilde{\varphi}$, $\tilde{\theta}$ are inverse to each other.*

Proof. Since the mapping $\theta\varphi = \mu$ is homotopic to the identity, it follows from A) that the homomorphism $\tilde{\mu}$ of $B^r(P)$ into itself is the identity isomorphism. According to Theorem 23, $\tilde{\mu} = \tilde{\theta}\tilde{\varphi}$, whence $\tilde{\theta}\tilde{\varphi}$ is the identity mapping of $B^r(P)$ onto itself. This implies that the kernel of $\tilde{\varphi}$ is zero and $\tilde{\theta}$ is a homomorphism of $B^r(Q)$ onto all of $B^r(P)$.

Similarly, the kernel of $\tilde{\theta}$ is zero and $\tilde{\varphi}$ is a homomorphism of $B^r(P)$ onto all of $B^r(Q)$. Comparing these results, it is seen that $\tilde{\varphi}$ and $\tilde{\theta}$ are inverse isomorphisms, which proves Theorem 24.

§16. The existence theorem for fixed points

In this section we shall give sufficient conditions for the existence of fixed points of a continuous mapping ω of a polyhedron P into itself. These conditions will be expressed in terms of the homology invariants of the mapping ω (see §15). The sufficient conditions cited here are known not to be necessary. It is known that necessary and sufficient conditions cannot be given in terms of the homology invariants alone. This is shown by rather complicated examples which cannot be adduced in this book. In addition to Theorem 27, we shall also prove Theorem 25. The latter is auxiliary to Theorem 27, but has other and deeper consequences.

The Trace of an Endomorphism of a Group

A) If B is a commutative group of finite rank, written additively,

$$x_1, \cdots, x_r$$

a maximal linearly independent system of elements of B, and x any element of B, then there exists a linear dependence

$$ax = a^1x_1 + \cdots + a^rx_r, \tag{1}$$

where a is a natural number, and $a^1, \cdots, a^r$ are integers. Set

$$\dot{a}^i = a^i/a$$

and, with no regard for group-theoretic meaning, write the formal equality

$$x \doteq \dot{a}^1x_1 + \cdots + \dot{a}^rx_r, \tag{2}$$

where $\dot{a}^1, \cdots, \dot{a}^r$ are rational numbers. Equation (2) merely means that, after multiplication by a suitable number a, it reduces to equation (1) which does have group-theoretic meaning. If a is a suitable number for the reduction of (2) to (1), then obviously every multiple of a also serves the same purpose. The numbers $\dot{a}^1, \cdots, \dot{a}^r$ do not, of course, determine the element x, but for a given system $x_1, \cdots, x_r$, the element x does uniquely determine the numbers $\dot{a}^1, \cdots, \dot{a}^r$. Let us prove this.

Assume that in addition to (2) we have

$$x \doteq \dot{b}^1 x_1 + \cdots + \dot{b}^r x_r \tag{3}$$

which, on multiplication by the natural number b, acquires group-theoretic meaning. Multiplication of (2) and (3) by ab yields the equations

$$\begin{aligned} abx &= ab\dot{a}^1 x_1 + \cdots + ab\dot{a}^r x_r , \\ abx &= ab\dot{b}^1 x_1 + \cdots + ab\dot{b}^r x_r , \end{aligned} \tag{4}$$

which have group-theoretic meaning. Since the system $x_1, \cdots, x_r$ is linearly independent, equations (4) yield the numerical equalities:

$$ab\dot{a}^i = ab\dot{b}^i, \qquad i = 1, \cdots, r;$$

whence $\dot{a}^i = \dot{b}^i$, and the assertion is proved.

B) A homomorphism of a group into itself is called an *endomorphism* of the group. Let B be a commutative group of finite rank, and let

$$x_1, \cdots, x_r$$

be a maximal system of linearly independent elements of B, and f an endomorphism of the group B. By A), we can write the relation

$$f(x_i) \doteq \sum_{j=1}^r \dot{a}^j_i \, x_j . \tag{5}$$

The trace $S(\| \dot{a}^j_i \|) = \sum_{i=1}^r \dot{a}^i_i$ of the matrix $\| \dot{a}^j_i \|$ is independent of the choice of the system $x_1, \cdots, x_r$ and hence is called the *trace of the endomorphism* f of the group B. It will be denoted by $S(f, B)$. We shall prove that $\sum_{i=1}^r \dot{a}^i_i$ is independent of the choice of the system $x_1, \cdots, x_r$. Let $y_1, \cdots, y_r$ be another system of linearly independent elements, and let

$$f(y_i) \doteq \sum_{j=1}^r \dot{b}^j_i \, y_j \tag{6}$$

be the equality analogous to (5). In addition, let

$$y_i \doteq \sum_{j=1}^r \dot{p}^j_i \, x_j , \tag{7}$$

$$x_i \doteq \sum_{j=1}^r \dot{q}^j_i \, y_j . \tag{8}$$

There is obviously a natural number a which on multiplication into (5), (6), (7), and (8) reduces these to expressions having group-theoretic meaning. Relations (7) and (8) yield

$$a^2 y_i = \sum_{j=1}^r a\dot{p}^j{}_i\, ax_j = \sum_{j,k=1}^r a\dot{p}^j{}_i\, a\dot{q}^k{}_j\, y_k, \text{ i.e., } y_i \doteq \sum_{j,k=1}^r \dot{p}^j{}_i\, \dot{q}^k{}_j\, y_k,$$

and since $y_i \doteq y_i$, it follows that

$$\sum_{j=1}^r \dot{p}^j{}_i\, \dot{q}^k{}_j = \delta^k{}_i. \tag{9}$$

Relations (8), (6), and (7) imply

$$a^3 f(x_i) = a^2 f(\sum_{j=1}^r a\dot{q}^j{}_i\, y_j) = a\sum_{j=1}^r a\dot{q}^j{}_i\, af(y_j) = a\sum_{j,k=1}^r a\dot{q}^j{}_i\, a\dot{b}^k{}_j\, y_k$$
$$= \sum_{j,k=1}^r a\dot{q}^j{}_i\, a\dot{b}^k{}_j\, ay_k = \sum_{j,k,l=1}^r a\dot{q}^j{}_i\, a\dot{b}^k{}_j\, a\dot{p}^l{}_k\, x_l,$$

whence

$$f(x_i) \doteq \sum_{j,k,l=1}^r \dot{q}^j{}_i\, \dot{b}^k{}_j\, \dot{p}^l{}_k\, x_l.$$

Comparing the last relation with (5), we get

$$\dot{a}^l{}_i = \sum_{j,k=1}^r \dot{q}^j{}_i\, \dot{b}^k{}_j\, \dot{p}^l{}_k.$$

We now have, by (9),

$$\sum_{l=1}^r \dot{a}^l{}_l = \sum_{j,k,l=1}^r \dot{q}^j{}_l\, \dot{b}^k{}_j\, \dot{p}^l{}_k = \sum_{j,k,l=1}^r \dot{p}^l{}_k\, \dot{q}^j{}_l\, \dot{b}^k{}_j = \sum_{l=1}^r \dot{b}^l{}_l,$$

which proves that the trace $S(f, B)$ is independent of the system

$$x_1, \cdots, x_r.$$

C) Let B be a group of finite rank, C a subgroup of B, and $B^* = B/C$ the corresponding factor group. If the subgroup C is invariant with respect to an endomorphism f of the group B, i.e., $f(C) \subset C$, then the endomorphism f is obviously also defined on C. Moreover, f can also be defined in a natural way on B^*; in order to do this, it suffices to set

$$f(x^*) = [f(x)]^*,$$

where $x^* \in B^*$, $x \in x^*$, and $[f(x)]^*$ is the element of B^* which contains $f(x)$. The resulting mapping $f(x^*)$ is independent of the choice of $x \in x^*$ and is an endomorphism of the group B^*. Furthermore, the traces of B, C, and B^* satisfy the following important relation:

$$S(f, B) = S(f, B^*) + S(f, C). \tag{10}$$

If x and x' are any two elements of x^*, then $x - x' \in C$ and

$$f(x) - f(x') = f(x - x') \in C.$$

Hence $f(x)$ and $f(x')$ are in the same coset of the subgroup C relative to the group B.

We shall now prove (10). Let $y_1, \cdots, y_t$ be a maximal linearly independent system of C, and $x^*_1, \cdots, x^*_s$ a maximal linearly independent system of B^*. Denoting by x_i an element of the coset x^*_i, the system $x_1, \cdots, x_s, y_1, \cdots, y_t$ is a maximal linearly independent system of the group B. This has already been proved (see §6, lemma). Hence, by A),

$$f(x_i) \doteq \sum_{k=1}^{s} \dot{a}^k{}_i x_k + \sum_{l=1}^{t} \dot{b}^l{}_i y_l, \tag{11}$$

and since $f(C) \subset C$, it follows that

$$f(y_j) \doteq \sum_{l=1}^{t} \dot{c}^l{}_j y_l. \tag{12}$$

Multiplying (11) by a suitable natural number a, rewriting the result in terms of the cosets, and dividing again by a, we obtain

$$f(x^*_i) \doteq \sum_{k=1}^{s} \dot{a}^k{}_i x^*_k. \tag{13}$$

Relations (11), (12), and (13) imply

$$S(f, B) = \sum_{k=1}^{s} \dot{a}^k{}_k + \sum_{l=1}^{t} \dot{c}^l{}_l,$$

$$S(f, C) = \sum_{l=1}^{t} \dot{c}^l{}_l, \qquad S(f, B^*) = \sum_{k=1}^{s} \dot{a}^k{}_k,$$

which proves (10).

D) Let B be a group of finite rank, C the subgroup of B consisting of all the elements of finite order of the group B, and let $\tilde{B} = B/C$. If f is any endomorphism of the group B, then obviously $f(C) \subset C$ and $S(f, C) = 0$, since C contains no independent elements. Hence the endomorphism f is defined on $\tilde{B}$ and $S(f, \tilde{B}) = S(f, B)$. We call the passage from the group B to the group $\tilde{B}$ a reduction. The reduced group $\tilde{B}$ obviously has no elements of finite order, other than zero.

Weak Homology

DEFINITION 26. Let K be a complex and let $Z^r{}_0$ be the group of r-cycles of K over the group of integers. Two cycles z_1 and z_2 of $Z^r{}_0$ are said to be *weakly homologous*, $z_1 \approx z_2$, if $a(z_1 - z_2) \sim 0$ for some natural number a. The set $\tilde{H}^r{}_0$ of all cycles weakly homologous to zero obviously forms a subgroup of $Z^r{}_0$, while the group $H^r{}_0$ of cycles homologous to zero is contained in $\tilde{H}^r{}_0$. The factor group $\tilde{B}^r = Z^r{}_0/\tilde{H}^r{}_0$ is called the *reduced Betti group* of the complex K. Its elements are classes of weakly homologous cycles.

E) Since $H^r{}_0 \subset \tilde{H}^r{}_0$ (see Def. 26), every coset z^* of the subgroup $H^r{}_0$ relative to the group $Z^r{}_0$ is contained in some coset $\tilde{z}$ of the subgroup $\tilde{H}^r{}_0$ relative to the group $Z^r{}_0$. The correspondence $z^* \to \tilde{z}$ obviously induces a homomorphism of the group $B^r{}_0$ onto the group $\tilde{B}^r$. The kernel of this homomorphism consists of all the elements of finite order of $B^r{}_0$, so that $\tilde{B}^r$ is the reduced group of the group $B^r{}_0$ (see D)). Therefore the trace of an arbitrary endomorphism of $B^r{}_0$ is equal to the trace of the corresponding endomorphism of $\tilde{B}^r$. This is the significance of the reduced Betti group.

Let us show that the kernel C^r of the homomorphism $z^* \to \tilde{z}$ is the set of elements of finite order of B^r_0. If $z^* \in C^r$ and $z \in z^*$, then $z \approx 0$, since

$$z \in z^* \subset \tilde{z} = 0.$$

Hence $az \sim 0$ for some natural number a, whence $az^* = 0$, i.e., z^* is of finite order. Conversely, if z^* is of finite order, then $az^* = 0$, whence $az \sim 0$ for an arbitrary cycle $z \in z^*$, i.e., $z \approx 0$. Hence $\tilde{z} = 0$, i.e., $z^* \in C^r$.

F) Since the group $\tilde{B}^r$ (see Def. 26) has no elements of finite order and admits of a finite system of generators, $\tilde{B}^r$ has a linearly independent basis $\tilde{z}_1, \cdots, \tilde{z}_p$. Let us choose a cycle z_i from each class $\tilde{z}_i$. The system of cycles $z_1, \cdots, z_p$ forms a so-called *weak homology basis* of dimension r of the complex K with the property that, if z is any r-cycle of K, then

$$z \approx a^1 z_1 + \cdots + a^p z_p,$$

where $a^1, \cdots, a^p$ are integers uniquely determined by z and the basis $z_1, \cdots, z_p$.

Let K and L be two complexes, K^α and L^β subdivisions of K and L, respectively, and f a simplicial mapping of K^α into L^β. It is clear that $z_1 \approx z_2$ in K^α implies $\hat{f}(z_1) \approx \hat{f}(z_2)$ in L^β. Hence the simplicial mapping f induces a homomorphism $\tilde{f}$ of the group $\tilde{B}^r(K)$ into the group $\tilde{B}^r(L)$ (see §12, A)). Now if $L^\beta = K$, then the endomorphism $\tilde{f}$ of the group $\tilde{B}^r$ and the endomorphism $\bar{f}$ of the group B^r_0 have identical traces (see D), E)). Their common trace can be obtained as follows: let $z^r_1, \cdots, z^r_{p(r)}$ be an r-dimensional weak homology basis of K, so that

$$\hat{f}[(z^r_i)^\alpha] \approx \textstyle\sum_{j=1}^{p(r)} {}^r a^j_i z^r_j. \tag{14}$$

Then

$$S[\bar{f}, B^r_0(K)] = S[\tilde{f}, \tilde{B}^r(K)] = \textstyle\sum_{j=1}^{p(r)} {}^r a^j_j. \tag{15}$$

In order to prove (15), denote by $\tilde{z}^r_i$ that weak homology class of K which contains the cycle z^r_i and apply relation (14) to the group $\tilde{B}^r(K)$. Then

$$\tilde{f}(\tilde{z}^r_i) = \textstyle\sum_{j=1}^{p(r)} {}^r a^j_i \tilde{z}^r_j. \tag{16}$$

Since $\tilde{z}^r_1, \cdots, \tilde{z}^r_{p(r)}$ is a maximal linearly independent system of $\tilde{B}^r(K)$, (16) implies (15).

The Euler-Poincaré-Hopf Formula

The theorem of Hopf which is given below serves as the basis for obtaining various theorems on fixed points, and is at the same time a direct generalization of the Euler-Poincaré theorem on the Euler characteristic.

THEOREM 25. *Let K be an n-complex, K^α a subdivision of K, and f a simplicial mapping of K^α into K. Denote by L^r_0 the group of all r-chains of K^α*

over the group of integers. If $x \in L^r{}_0$ *and* $g(x) = [\hat{f}(x)]^\alpha$, *then* g *is an endomorphism of* $L^r{}_0$ *and* f *induces the endomorphism* $\tilde{f}$ *of* $\tilde{B}^r(K)$ (see G)). *Under these conditions, it follows that*

$$(17)\quad \sum_{r=0}^{n} (-1)^r S(g, L^r{}_0) = \sum_{r=0}^{n} (-1)^r S[\tilde{f}, \tilde{B}^r(K)] = J(f, K).$$

Proof. The endomorphism g is defined on $L^r{}_0$ for arbitrary r, $r = 0, 1, \cdots, n$. If $x \in L^r{}_0$, then

$$(18)\qquad \Delta g(x) = g(\Delta x),$$

since

$$\Delta g(x) = \Delta[\hat{f}(x)]^\alpha = [\Delta \hat{f}(x)]^\alpha = [\hat{f}(\Delta x)]^\alpha = g(\Delta x).$$

Denote by $Z^r{}_0$ the subgroup of cycles of $L^r{}_0$ and by $H^r{}_0$ the subgroup of cycles homologous to zero of $L^r{}_0$. Relation (18) immediately implies that

$$(19)\qquad g(Z^r{}_0) \subset Z^r{}_0, \qquad g(H^r{}_0) \subset H^r{}_0.$$

This, by B), implies that

$$(20)\quad S(g, L^r{}_0) = S(g, Z^r{}_0) + S(g, L^r{}_0/Z^r{}_0)$$
$$= S(g, Z^r{}_0/H^r{}_0) + S(g, H^r{}_0) + S(g, L^r{}_0/Z^r{}_0).$$

Let us clarify the meaning of the endomorphism g as applied to the groups $Z^r{}_0/H^r{}_0 = B^r{}_0(K^\alpha)$ and $L^r{}_0/Z^r{}_0$, bearing in mind the fact that there exists a well-defined isomorphism between $B^r{}_0(K^\alpha)$ and $B^r{}_0(K)$, as well as between $L^r{}_0/Z^r{}_0$ and H_0^{r-1}.

The simplicial mapping f associates with each cycle z^α of K^α a cycle $\hat{f}(z^\alpha)$ of K and in this way induces an endomorphism $\tilde{f}$ of $B^r{}_0(K)$ (see C)). If we now wish to pass from the group $B^r{}_0(K)$ to the group $B^r{}_0(K^\alpha)$ by means of a natural isomorphism (see Theorem 15), we must assign a cycle $[\hat{f}(z^\alpha)]^\alpha$ to the cycle z^α of K^α. This mapping coincides with g. Hence the endomorphism $\tilde{f}$ of $B^r{}_0(K)$ is transformed into an endomorphism g of $Z^r{}_0/H^r{}_0$ by means of the natural isomorphism between $B^r{}_0(K)$ and

$$Z^r{}_0/H^r{}_0 = B^r{}_0(K^\alpha).$$

Thus

$$(21)\qquad S[\tilde{f}, B^r{}_0(K)] = S[g, Z^r{}_0/H^r{}_0].$$

Let x^* be any element of $L^r{}_0/Z^r{}_0$ and x any chain of the coset x^*. Since all elements of x^* have identical boundaries, we can set $\Delta x^* = \Delta x$. The mapping Δ so defined is an isomorphism of $L^r{}_0/Z^r{}_0$ onto H_0^{r-1}, since the kernel of the homomorphism Δ of L^r_0 onto H_0^{r-1} is Z^r_0. The endomorphism g is defined on L^r_0/Z^r_0 as well as on $H_0^{r-1} \subset L_0^{r-1}$ (see C) and (19)). Since, by (18), $g(\Delta x^*) = \Delta g(x^*)$, it follows that the endomorphism g is the same on H_0^{r-1} and on L^r_0/Z^r_0, provided that the transition from H_0^{r-1} to L^r_0/Z^r_0 is effected by means of the isomorphism Δ. Hence

$$(22) \qquad S(g, L^r_0/Z^r_0) = S(g, H_0^{r-1}).$$

In the light of (21) and (22) we may rewrite (20) in the form

$$(23) \qquad S(g, L^r_0) = S[\tilde{f}, B^r_0(K)] + S(g, H^r_0) + S(g, H_0^{r-1}),$$

where we must put $S(g, H^n_0) = S(g, H_0^{-1}) = 0$. Multiplication of (23) by $(-1)^r$ and summation over r yields

$$\sum_{r=0}^{n} (-1)^r S(g, L^r_0) = \sum_{r=0}^{n} (-1)^r S[\tilde{f}, B^r_0(K)].$$

Since the equality $S[\tilde{f}, \tilde{B}^r(K)] = S[\tilde{f}, B^r_0(K)]$ was noted previously (see G)), the proof of Theorem 25 is complete.

H) If $A^r_1, \cdots, A^r_{\alpha(r)}$ is the set of all oriented r-simplexes of the complex K^α, $r = 0, 1, \cdots, n$, then $\hat{f}(A^r_j)$ is an oriented r-simplex of K or 0, and $[\hat{f}(A^r_j)]^\alpha$ is of the form

$$(24) \qquad [\hat{f}(A^r_j)]^\alpha = \sum_{k=1}^{\alpha(r)} {}^r f^k_j A^r_k,$$

where the coefficients ${}^r f^k_j$ are all integers. We shall show that

$$(25) \quad J(f, K) = \sum_{r=0}^{n} (-1)^r \sum_{k=1}^{\alpha(r)} {}^r f^k_k = \sum_{r=0}^{n} (-1)^r \sum_{l=1}^{p(r)} {}^r a^l_l.$$

In order to prove (25), note that $A^r_1, \cdots, A^r_{\alpha(r)}$ is a maximal linearly independent system of L^r_0, whence $S(g, L^r_0) = \sum_{k=1}^{\alpha(r)} {}^r f^k_k$. Since (15) and (17) also hold, the proof of H) is complete.

Let us now derive the Euler-Poincaré formula from (25). If $K^\alpha = K$ and f is the identity mapping of K onto itself, then (24) can be replaced by $\hat{f}(A^r_j) = A^r_j$, whence in this case, ${}^r f^k_j = \delta^k_j$, i.e., $\sum_{k=1}^{\alpha(r)} {}^r f^k_k = \alpha(r)$. Similarly, in this case, (14) can be replaced by $\hat{f}(z^r_i) = z^r_i$, so that

$$\sum_{l=1}^{p(r)} {}^r a^l_l = p(r)$$

and therefore $\sum_{r=0}^{n} (-1)^r \alpha(r) = \sum_{r=0}^{n} (-1)^r p(r)$.

The Existence Theorem

THEOREM 26. *If φ is a continuous mapping of an n-complex K into itself, then φ has a fixed point provided that the number*

$$J(\varphi, K) = \sum_{r=0}^{n} (-1)^r S[\tilde{\varphi}, \tilde{B}^r(K)]$$

does not vanish. Here $\tilde{\varphi}$ is the endomorphism of $\tilde{B}^r(K)$ induced by φ (see G) and Theorem 20).

Proof. The proof is by contradiction. We shall assume that φ has no fixed points and show that then $J(\varphi, K) = 0$.

If φ has no fixed points, since $|K|$ is compact, there exists a positive ε such that

$$\rho[x, \varphi(x)] > \varepsilon \qquad \text{for } x \in |K|. \tag{26}$$

Let K^β be a subdivision of K so fine that the diameter of every simplex of K^β is less than $\varepsilon/3$. In order not to change the notation used above, let $K^\beta = K$. This merely means that K was originally taken with a sufficiently fine subdivision. Now let K^α be a subdivision of K so fine as to admit of a simplicial approximation f to φ of K^α into K. Since, for each $x \in |K|$, there is a simplex $D \in K$ such that $f(x) \in D$ and $\varphi(x) \in D$, it follows that $\rho[f(x), \varphi(x)] < \varepsilon/3$. Hence by (26),

$$\rho[x, f(x)] > \tfrac{2}{3}\varepsilon. \tag{27}$$

If $A^r{}_j$ is any oriented simplex of K^α, then the simplexes $f(A^r{}_j)$ and $A^r{}_j$ are disjoint. Indeed, if for $x \in A^r{}_j$ and $f(x) \in f(A^r{}_j)$, $A^r{}_j$ were to intersect $f(A^r{}_j)$, then we would have $\rho[x, f(x)] < \frac{2}{3}\varepsilon$, since the diameters of both simplexes are less than $\varepsilon/3$.

If, in relation (24), at least one of the numbers ${}^r f^j{}_j$ is different from zero, then the simplex $A^r{}_j$ is contained in $\hat{f}(A^r{}_j)^\alpha$, i.e., $A^r{}_j$ intersects $f(A^r{}_j)$, which is impossible. Hence every coefficient ${}^r f^j{}_j$ vanishes and $J(f, K) = 0$. In order to show that this is also true of $J(\varphi, K)$, it is merely necessary to note that the endomorphism $\tilde{\varphi}$, by construction, is the same as the endomorphism $\tilde{f}$. Hence $J(\varphi, K) = 0$. This proves Theorem 26.

The corresponding theorem for a polyhedron P follows immediately from Theorem 26. The reduced Betti group $\tilde{B}^r(P)$ of the polyhedron P can be defined as the reduction of the group $B^r{}_0(P)$ (see D)), or else by means of triangulations, as was done in Def. 22. If ω is a continuous mapping of the polyhedron P into itself, it induces an endomorphism $\tilde{\omega}$ of $\tilde{B}^r(P)$. The endomorphism $\tilde{\omega}$ may be defined either as in remark D) or as in Theorem 22.

THEOREM 27. *If ω is a continuous mapping of an n-dimensional polyhedron P into itself, then ω has a fixed point provided that*

$$J(\omega, P) = \sum_{r=0}^{n} (-1)^r S[\tilde{\omega}, \tilde{B}^r(P)]$$

does not vanish, where $\tilde{\omega}$ is the endomorphism of $\tilde{B}^r(P)$ induced by ω.

Proof. If (σ, K) is any triangulation of the polyhedron P, then

$$\varphi = \sigma^{-1}\omega\sigma$$

is a continuous mapping of the complex K into itself. It is clear that $J(\omega, P) = J(\varphi, K)$, so that $J(\varphi, K) \neq 0$. Hence φ has a fixed point x (see Theorem 26), and $\sigma(x) \in P$ is a fixed point of ω. Indeed,

$$\omega[\sigma(x)] = \sigma[\varphi(x)] = \sigma(x),$$

which proves Theorem 27.

I) If φ is a continuous mapping of a connected complex K into itself, then $S[\tilde{f}, \tilde{B}^0(K)] = 1$.

Indeed, let f be a simplicial approximation to φ of K^α into K. If a is a vertex of K, then $+(a)$ is a cycle which generates a zero-dimensional weak homology basis in K. Since $\hat{f}[+(a)] = +(b)$, where b is likewise a vertex of K, it follows that $\hat{f}[+(a)] \approx +(a)$, whence by G), $S[\tilde{f}, \tilde{B}^0(K)] = 1$.

THEOREM 28. *If A is a simplex of arbitrary dimension and ω is an arbitrary continuous mapping of A into itself, then $J(\omega, A) = 1$. Hence ω has a fixed point* (see Theorem 14).

Proof. In virtue of I), $S[\tilde{\omega}, \tilde{B}^0(A)] = 1$. Moreover, since for $r > 0$ the group $\tilde{B}^r(A)$ has no elements different from zero, we have $J(\omega, A) = 1$. This proves Theorem 28.

J) Let R^{n+1}, $n \geqq 1$, be the $(n + 1)$-dimensional Euclidean space with Cartesian coordinates $x^1, x^2, \cdots, x^{n+1}$. The set Σ^n of points of R^{n+1} satisfying the equation $(x^1)^2 + (x^2)^2 + \cdots + (x^{n+1})^2 = 1$, called an n-sphere, is homeomorphic to the frontier $F^n = | S^n |$ of an $(n + 1)$-simplex. Hence Σ^n is a polyhedron whose n-dimensional Betti group is the free cyclic group. If u is a generator of this group and ω is a continuous mapping of the polyhedron Σ^n into itself, then $\tilde{\omega}(u) = ku$. The number k is called the degree of the mapping (Abbildungsgrad) ω of Σ^n into itself. It is an invariant of the mapping class which contains ω.

In order to prove that Σ^n and F^n are homeomorphic, choose an $(n + 1)$-simplex A^{n+1} in R^{n+1} whose center is at the origin of coordinates O of R^{n+1} and such that $\Sigma^n \subset A^{n+1}$. If $x \in F^n$ (where F^n is the frontier of A^{n+1}), then the segment (O, x) intersects Σ^n in a single point $y = \varphi(x)$. It is easily seen that φ is a homeomorphism of F^n onto Σ^n.

THEOREM 29. *If ω is a continuous mapping of an n-sphere Σ^n into itself* (see J)) *of degree k, then $J(\omega, \Sigma^n) = 1 + (-1)^n k$. Hence ω always has a fixed point provided that the number $1 + (-1)^n k$ does not vanish.*

Theorem 29 is an immediate consequence of Theorem 27 and the fact that the Betti groups of dimension r, $0 < r < n$, of the complex S^n are all trivial, while its zero- and n-dimensional Betti groups are free cyclic groups (see Theorem 11).

As a simple application of Theorem 29, consider the mapping ω of Σ^n into itself which maps each point $x \in \Sigma^n$ into its diametrically opposite point, $-x$, i.e., $\omega(x) = -x$. This mapping obviously has no fixed points, and hence the number $1 + (-1)^n k$ is equal to zero, so that $k = (-1)^{n+1}$, i.e., the degree of the mapping of Σ^n into itself which maps every point into its diametrically opposite one is $(-1)^{n+1}$.

LIST OF DEFINITIONS

LIST OF THEOREMS

BASIC LITERATURE ON COMBINATORIAL TOPOLOGY

1. ALEXANDROFF, P., UND HOPF, H. *Topologie*, I, Berlin, Springer, 1935, (Grundlehren der mathematischen Wissenschaften, Bd. 45). Reprinted by Edwards Brothers, Ann Arbor, Michigan, 1945.
2. ALEKSANDROV, P. S. *Kombinatornaya Topologiya* (Combinatorial Topology), Moscow-Leningrad, 1947, (Russian).
3. SEIFERT, H., UND THRELFALL, W. *Lehrbuch der Topologie*, Berlin, Teubner, 1934. Reprinted by Chelsea, New York, 1947.
4. LEFSCHETZ, S. *Algebraic Topology*, New York, 1942, (American Mathematical Society, Colloquium Publications, vol. 27).

ADDITIONAL REFERENCES*

1. ALEKSANDROV, P. S., AND EFREMOVITCH, V. A. *Očerk Osnovnych Ponyatiĭ Topologii* (Sketch of the Fundamental Notions of Topology), Moscow-Leningrad, 1936.
2. HAUSDORFF, F. *Mengenlehre*, 3rd edition, Berlin, 1935. Reprinted by Dover Publications, New York, 1944.
3. ALEKSANDROV, P. S., AND KOLMOGOROV, A. N. *Vvedenie v teoriyu množestv i teoriyu funkciĭ. Čast' pervaya* (Introduction to the Theory of Sets and the Theory of Functions. Part One), Moscow-Leningrad, 1948.
4. KUROŠ, A. G. *Teoriya Grupp* (Theory of Groups), Moscow-Leningrad, 1944. Chelsea reports a translation of this book in preparation.
5. ALEXANDROFF, P. *Einfachste Grundbegriffe der Topologie*, Berlin, Springer, 1932. This book is listed as a substitute for Aleksandrov-Efremovitch. It has been reprinted by Ungar Publishing Co., N. Y.
6. LEFSCHETZ, S. *Introduction to Topology*, Princeton University Press, 1949, (Princeton Mathematical Series, no. 11).
7. NEWMAN, M. H. A. *Elements of the Topology of Plane Sets of Points*, 2nd edition, Cambridge University Press, 1951.
8. PONTRYAGIN, L. *Topological Groups*, Princeton University Press, 1939, (Princeton Mathematical Series, no. 2). Chapter I of this book contains an account of all the group-theoretic material required in the present book, especially a clear proof of the theorem on the decomposition of commutative groups.
9. EILENBERG, S. AND STEENROD, N. *Foundations of Algebraic Topology*, Princeton University Press, 1952, (Princeton Mathematical Series, no. 15).

* The first four titles are mentioned in the text, the last five have been added by the translators.

INDEX